Alexander
and the Golden Bird

GW00985801

For Julia and Louisa

ALEXANDER AND THE GOLDEN BIRD

AND OTHER DANISH FOLK TALES

Translated and retold from the Danish
by Reginald Spink

With illustrations by Carol Peel

Floris Books

First published by Floris Books in 1991.
© 1991 Reginald Spink
All rights reserved. No part of this publication may
be reproduced without the prior permission of
Floris Books, 15 Harrison Gardens, Edinburgh

British Library CIP Data available

ISBN 0–86315–115–9
Printed in Great Britain by Dotesios Ltd, Trowbridge, Wilts.

Contents

A simpleton

There was once a widow whose only son was very simple. One day, after he had watched her churning butter, the boy asked his mother if he could take some of the butter to town and sell it. Now, he had never been to town before, so she found this rather a foolish idea; but as he begged and pleaded for her to let him go, she at last agreed and gave him a little of the butter.

"Now, be off," she said. And off he went.

Walking along the road, he came to a large rock by the wayside; and thinking, in his simplicity, that this was the town, he asked the rock if it would like to buy some of his mother's butter. The rock said never a word.

"Now, look here, town," said the boy, "this is good butter I'm selling. Taste it."

With that, he smeared a little of the butter on the rock; and as the sun was shining, it melted and the boy thought the town was eating the butter.

"Well," he said, "you seem to like my mother's butter, town. Have it all. I can come for the money tomorrow."

So saying, he smeared the rest of the butter on the rock and went off home.

In answer to his mother's question about what he had done with the butter, and what he had got for it, the boy said: "I sold it to the town, and I'm going back to get the money tomorrow."

"What?" she said. "You sold it to the town? That's a fine tale, I must say. What I would like to know is who bought it in the town?"

"I tell you, Mother, I sold it to the town, just as I said."

"Oh, all right, then," she said. "You sold it to the town, and we'll say no more about it. I should have had more sense than to give it to you."

The next day, the boy went off to get his money and, arriving at the rock, said: "Well, town, I've come for my money for the butter I sold you yesterday."

But the rock said never a word.

The boy now began to lose his temper.

"You cheating old town," he cried. "You bought some butter from me, and now you won't pay me for it, and you won't even answer me! Who do you think I am? I'll soon show you!"

And he hit out at the rock, and pummelled and pushed it till it rolled over. And what do you think he found underneath it? A pot full of money. Delighted to have got payment for his butter at last, he tucked the pot under his arm and went off home.

His mother could hardly believe her own eyes when she saw all these riches.

"Where did you get the money from, my son?" she asked.

"From the town, Mother, of course," he said. "It wouldn't pay me what it owed me, and when it wouldn't even answer me I knocked it down and took the money."

"What's all this, you silly boy? You knocked the

town down? I can just see you! However, you got the money, so never mind!"

Well, time passed, and one day the woman killed a pig, and her son said he would go to town and sell some of the bacon. So off he went, with the bacon in a basket. This time he really arrived at the town, and as he entered it a pack of dogs came barking at him.

"Hello!" said the boy. "Would you like some bacon?"

The dogs only barked.

"Taste it!" he said.

And when they had gobbled the piece up and seemed to like it, he emptied the rest of the bacon for them, saying he would come and get his money the next day.

In the town the next day he met the dogs again; and after saying "Hello!" to them, asked for his money. The dogs only barked.

"What?" said the boy. "You're not going to pay me? I'll show you, you dirty dogs!"

Among the pack there was a little dog that was wearing a very fine collar; and thinking that this was the master of the pack, he drove it into an alley-way and caught it. Then, with the dog under his arm, he set off for the palace, meaning to complain to the king about it and the other dogs.

Now, the king had a very beautiful daughter, but she was very sad and serious, and he had proclaimed that whoever made her laugh should have her for his wife and should reign when he died.

Of course, the first person the boy met when he arrived at the palace was a sentry, and the sentry refused to let him pass until he had learnt his errand.

"I've been robbed of my bacon," said the boy, "and I want to complain to the king about it, so as to get my money."

The sentry then said that he would let him pass if he would agree to give him half of what he got, which the boy did.

He then came to another sentry, who before allowing him to pass made him promise to give him a quarter of what he got.

Soon he came to a third sentry, who made the boy promise to give him the last quarter of what he got.

So in the end he was admitted to the palace, and the king came forward to receive him.

"Well," said the king, when the boy had explained his trouble, "*you* sold the bacon to the dogs, and you'll have to get paid for it. I can't help you there."

Meanwhile, the king's daughter had been standing

by and had heard all that had been said, and she could not help laughing.

"Aha!" said the king, "now you've made my daughter laugh, so now I'm going to pay you. She's yours."

"But I don't want your daughter," said the boy.

"You don't want my daughter!" cried the king. "All right, then. I'll give you some money. To tell the truth, I'd rather do that."

"I don't want your money, either," the boy replied.

"You don't want my money?" the astonished king cried. "Then what do you want?"

"I want sixty lashes," the boy said.

"Why, with pleasure," the king said. "That's easy. Come here!"

And turning to one of his footmen, he told him to give the boy his sixty lashes.

"Oh, no, not me," said the boy. "I owe them to the sentries. The first sentry made me promise to give him half of what I got, and the others made me promise them a quarter each."

So each of the sentries got his agreed share of the sixty lashes.

"I see," said the king, "that you aren't such a simpleton as you seem to be. Do you still refuse my daughter?"

"No," said the boy; "now the sentries have had their share, I'll have her."

So the widow's simple son got the princess and inherited the kingdom when the king died. With his queen, he lives happily to this day in the royal palace.

Which goes to show that, for a simpleton, he didn't do so badly, after all.

The fat cat

Once upon a time an old woman was busy making porridge in her kitchen when suddenly she remembered a message she had to give to her neighbour.

So she asked the cat to look after her porridge while she was away.

"All right," said the cat; "just leave that to me."

Now when the old woman had gone, the cat took a sniff at the porridge and, thinking that it smelt very nice, ate up both the porridge and the pot with it.

Soon the old woman came back from the neighbour's, and finding her porridge gone she said to the cat: "Whatever has happened to my porridge?"

"Why," said the cat, "I've eaten it, and the pot as well; and now I'm going to eat you."

And with that she ate up the old woman.

Then going off on her way she met Shoe Hottentot.

And Shoe Hottentot said to the cat: "What have you eaten, little cat, that makes you so fat?"

And the cat replied: "I've eaten both the porridge and the pot and the old woman, and now I'm going to eat you."

And with that she ate up Shoe Hottentot.

Then going off on her way she met Shoe Tommy-Tot.

And Shoe Tommy-Tot said to her: "Whatever have you eaten, little cat, that makes you so fat?"

"I've eaten both the porridge and the pot and the old woman and Shoe Hottentot," said the cat, "and now I'm going to eat you."

And with that she ate up Shoe Tommy-Tot.

Then going on her way she met five birds of a feather.

And the five birds of a feather said to her: "Whatever have you eaten, little cat, that makes you so fat?"

"I've eaten both the porridge and the pot and the old woman and Shoe Hottentot and Shoe Tommy-Tot," said the cat, "and now I'm going to eat you as well."

And with that she ate up five birds of a feather.

Then going on her way she met seven maids a-dancing.

And they said to her: "Why, what on earth have you eaten, little cat, that makes you so fat?"

And the cat replied: "I've eaten both the porridge and the pot and the old woman and Shoe Hottentot and Shoe Tommy-Tot and five birds of a feather, and now I'm going to eat you as well."

And with that she ate up seven maids a-dancing.

Then going on her way she met madam with her white flounce.

And madam with her white flounce said to her: "Dear me, what have you eaten, little cat, that makes you so fat?"

"Why," said the cat, "I've eaten both the porridge and the pot and the old woman and Shoe Hottentot and Shoe Tommy-Tot and five birds of a feather and seven maids a-dancing, and now I'm going to eat you as well."

And with that she ate up madam with her white flounce.

Then going on her way she met the parson with his crooked walking-stick.

And he said to her: "Why, what have you eaten, little cat, that makes you so fat?"

And the cat replied: "I've eaten both the porridge and the pot and the old woman and Shoe Hottentot and Shoe Tommy-Tot and five birds of a feather and seven maids a-dancing and madam with her white flounce, and now I'm going to eat you."

And with that she ate up the parson with his crooked walking-stick.

Then going on her way she met a woodcutter with his axe.

And the woodcutter said to the cat: "What on earth have you eaten, little cat, that makes you so fat?"

And the cat replied: "I've eaten both the porridge and the pot and the old woman and Shoe Hottentot and Shoe Tommy-Tot and five birds of a feather and seven maids a-dancing and madam with her white flounce and the parson with his crooked walking-stick, and now I'm going to eat you."

"Aha! that's just where you're wrong, little cat," said the woodcutter. And lifting his great big axe he chopped the cat right in half.

Then out ran the parson with his crooked walking-stick and madam with her white flounce and seven maids a-dancing and five birds of a feather and Shoe Tommy-Tot and Shoe Hottentot and the old woman. And seizing her pot and her porridge, the old woman hurried off home to her kitchen.

The golden apple

Many years ago there was a rich man who had three daughters, of whom he was very fond, though the one he loved best was the youngest.

One day when he was going to the fair he asked each of his three daughters what he should bring them back as presents from the fair. The eldest daughter said she would like a golden spinning-wheel, the middle daughter wanted a golden bobbin, and the youngest daughter asked for a golden apple.

Promising that he would do what he could to grant their various wishes, the man rode off to the fair.

After finishing his business, he succeeded in obtaining a golden spinning-wheel for his eldest daughter and a golden bobbin for his middle daughter; but try as he would, he could nowhere find a golden apple. Thus, though the two eldest daughters got their presents, the youngest went without one, because there were no golden apples to be had. She said, however, that her father was not to worry; sooner or later one would be found.

Some time after, a stranger came to the rich man's house and asked permission to marry his youngest daughter; but the man said that he would not part with his favourite, and that the eldest daughter was to marry first.

So in the end the stranger agreed to take the eldest daughter instead, and all arrangements were made for her to return with him to his house.

The family saw her off at the gate and she took her place beside him in the carriage that stood waiting.

As they drove off together, the stranger cried:

> Light in front and dark at the rear;
> Let no-one see where we go from here!

And no-one did see where they went.

In time the carriage arrived at a wood, and when it was almost too dark to see anything at all, they stopped at what the eldest daughter took to be a small cottage, and there they got out.

Inside the cottage, the stranger gave her a comfortable chair to sit on, and asked her if she had ever sat on anything that was softer.

"No," she replied, "never."

Next he gave her a pleasant drink, and asked her if she had ever tasted anything sweeter.

"No," she replied, "never."

When he heard this the stranger refused to have her for his wife, but took her back to her father and drove off with the middle daughter instead.

Exactly the same things happened to the middle daughter as had happened to the eldest daughter: they arrived at the cottage in the wood; the stranger gave her a comfortable chair to sit on and a pleasant drink to drink; and when she replied "No" to both his questions, he refused to keep her but drove her back to her father.

The rich man now agreed to let his youngest

daughter marry the stranger. So, like her sisters, she drove off with him into the wood; they stopped at what appeared to be a cottage; and giving her a comfortable chair to sit on, he asked if she had ever sat on anything softer.

"Yes," she replied, "when I sat on my mother's lap."

Then he gave her a pleasant drink and asked her if she had ever tasted anything sweeter.

"Yes," she replied, "when I sat at my mother's breast."

When he heard this the stranger was very happy, feeling sure that now he had found the right daughter for his wife.

When the youngest daughter woke the next morning, a most wonderful change had taken place: the little cottage had been transformed into a splendid palace, and everything in it was of the purest gold. The most wonderful thing of all, however, was the garden, which she saw through the window; for there, on a golden tree, hung golden apples.

She was still marvelling at the sight when the door opened and in came the stranger who, as you will have guessed, was a prince.

So she told him how she had long wanted a golden apple, and how her father had been unable to get one for her. The prince then went straight into the garden and picked, not one apple, but three; and the youngest daughter was very happy because she had now obtained her heart's desire.

One day she asked the prince if they might visit her father, whom she thought would be longing to see her; so they drove off in the carriage.

Her father had indeed missed his favourite daughter and was overjoyed to see her again. When she showed him the golden apples he was even happier, knowing that the stranger was a true prince; and he held a magnificent feast for them which lasted for many days, and at which everyone had a splendid time.

Greylegs and the proud princess

There was once a king of England whose daughter was famous for her beauty, though she was also both proud and very conceited. Men came from all over the world to court her, but she would never have anything at all to do with them. They were no match for her, she always said, and she would send them packing with many a harsh word.

Reports of the princess's beauty reached the ears of the young prince of Denmark, and he sent messengers to ask for her hand in marriage. The answer they got was that, sooner than marry a beggarly prince like him, she would spend the rest of her life spinning wool.

But the Danish prince was not to be put off. He sent other messengers, and they took with them a fine gift of six milk-white horses, all with pink muzzles, and every one of them shod with shoes of gold and saddled with crimson saddles. Such fine horses had never been seen in England before and the king praised the prince who had sent his daughter such royal presents.

But the hard-hearted princess ordered her stablemen to cut off the horses' beautiful manes and tails, bespatter them with mud, and send them back to Denmark; and she informed the messengers that, sooner than marry such a beggarly prince as their master, she would go selling pots and pans in the street.

When the king of Denmark heard this he was furious and would have despatched his fleet to punish the proud princess. But the prince urged him to be patient, saying he would try again and, if the next attempt failed, he would certainly take his revenge.

So the prince built a great ship, the richest and most gorgeous ship that had ever been seen. It was carved from end to end with the figures of animals and decorated with sheets of gold, while its red and white sails were all of silk. The prince sent this ship off to England, manned with the handsomest crew in the whole of his father's kingdom.

The splendid ship drew admiring crowds as it lay anchored near to the English palace, and the king did his best to persuade his daughter that she should accept the prince's gracious offer.

The princess now said she would think the matter over, promising the prince's messengers her reply in the morning. But then she wickedly commanded her servants to sink the ship in the night, telling the messengers the next morning they could find their way home as best they could. As for marrying the beggarly prince, she would sooner go begging her bread from door to door.

Somehow or other, the messengers succeeded in getting back to Denmark, where they told the sad story of how the magnificent ship now lay, with all its gold and costly silk, at the bottom of the sea. The Danish king would have set out at once to avenge this fresh insult to his son, but once again the prince urged him to be patient, saying he would make the princess repent of what she had done.

The prince now set out for England himself, disguised in old grey clothes as a beggar, wearing a battered hat and clogs, and carrying his other belongings in a bundle over his shoulder. On arrival at the English palace, he asked his way to the cowsheds, where he begged his supper and a night's lodging from the cowman, and that night slept with the cows.

Next morning the prince, who said his name was Greylegs, offered to water the cows for the friendly cowman, and he drove them off with a gold spindle that he took from his bundle.

The pool lay just below the princess's window, and she saw the prince drive the cattle down to drink. She also saw the gold spindle, and sent one of her maids to ask if Greylegs would sell it to her. The prince replied that she must ask him herself. Though hating the very idea, the princess was bent on getting the spindle, and so she allowed Greylegs to come into the hall outside her room. She then offered him a good price for the spindle. His reply was that he had no use for her money, but that he would give her the spindle if she would allow him to sleep outside her bedroom door.

"Certainly not!" said the princess.

"Then there's no more to talk about," replied the prince, "and I shall keep my spindle."

But the princess was determined to have the spindle, and so she talked the matter over with her maids, who promised to sit up and watch, so that no harm should befall her. And so it was arranged. That night the prince climbed the stairs, with his clogs under his arm, and lay down to sleep outside the princess's door, while the maids watched. But the princess never got a wink of sleep thinking of the horrid grey beggar outside her door, even though he slept quietly enough and left early again the next morning.

That morning the prince again helped the cowman to water his cattle at the pool, and, watching him from her window, the princess saw that this time he was driving them with a gold bobbin.

That gold bobbin was just the thing to go with her gold spindle, she thought, and so, just as she had done before, she sent her maids to ask the beggar what he would take for it. And, as before, the prince said she must ask him herself. So again the princess agreed to receive him in the hall outside her room. When she offered to buy the bobbin from him, the prince replied that she could have it for nothing if she would allow him to sleep inside her room that night.

"Never!" cried the princess.

But when he turned to go, and as she was very eager to have the bobbin, she talked the matter over with her maids, who promised to keep watch by her bed. So in the end she agreed.

That night the prince tiptoed up the stairs in his stockinged feet, with his clogs under his arm, and gave the bobbin to the waiting maids.

They then showed him to the place just inside the door at the end of the room where he was to sleep, and settled down themselves with their needlework in the middle of the room.

The maids, of course, were very sleepy after their long watch the night before and, now and then, they began to nod a little, though they managed to keep awake. As for the prince, he slept soundly all through the night, and rising early the next morning gathered up his clogs and crept quietly away down the stairs. But the princess never got a wink of sleep for thinking of the ugly beggar lying there at the other end of the room. She was very glad when it was all over, though delighted to think that she had got such a fine spindle and such a beautiful bobbin all for nothing.

Looking out of the window that morning, she saw the beggar driving the cows down to the water again, this time with a golden shuttle. That would be the very thing to go with her spindle and bobbin, she thought, and she was determined to get it. So she sent her maids as before and, as before, the prince said she would have to talk to him about it. So back they went to the princess, the prince this time going with them into the princess's room.

"Well, Greylegs," said the princess, "what will you take for that shuttle? I'll give you a hundred florins."

"No money can buy it," Greylegs replied. "But you can have it for nothing if you will let me sleep by your bedside."

"The fellow's mad!" the princess exclaimed. "I'll give you two hundred florins," she added.

"If Your Royal Highness wants the shuttle," said the prince, "you will have to pay me what I ask. Take it or leave it."

The princess turned to her maids and they all looked at the shuttle and thought how beautiful it was. Then, after talking the matter over with the maids, she said she would agree to the price. They would sit up and watch at her bedside.

That night the prince crept up the palace steps in his stockinged feet as before, and lay by the princess's bed while the maids kept watch. But after two sleepless nights they were very tired indeed, and when the prince was sound asleep and the princess was asleep too, their candles dropped one by one from their hands, and soon they were all fast asleep as well.

Having lost so much sleep on the first two nights, both the princess and her maids overslept the next morning, and were still asleep at midday. By then the king felt rather worried, and so he went round to the princess's bedroom to see what was the matter.

A strange sight met his gaze when he opened the bedroom door. The first he set eyes on were the maids, who all lay curled up fast asleep in their chairs. At his daughter's bedside lay a ragged coat, an old hat and a pair of clogs. His daughter was fast asleep in bed, and beside her lay a dirty beggar.

The king of England was as sad as he was angry to see all this, and his cries roused the princess and her maids. The maids all fled, too frightened for words. To the princess the king said: "So you have made your choice.' You can marry that fellow and go off with him. Never let me see you in this palace again!"

And after the wedding the king turned them both out into the street.

They fetched the prince's bundle and stick from the cowshed, and the princess changed from her royal robes into some rough woollen things that would be more suitable for the road, the prince told her. Then off they went.

Trudging along beside the man she had married, the princess at last began to take notice of him; walking there, clean and washed, he somehow seemed different from the dirty cattle man and, for all his old clothes, really rather handsome.

Being a princess, she was not used to walking; and as the road was rough and she was wearing heavy clogs, she soon grew tired and footsore. She had to sit down and rest.

"Don't leave me, Greylegs!" she begged.

"I'm not going to leave you," the prince said, "now I've got you at last."

But when his wife could not walk any further, he hired a wagon and some straw for her to sit on, and they made for the nearest harbour, where they embarked on board a ship that lay there. The princess had not the least idea where they were going, nor did she now care very much.

Needless to say, however, they sailed straight to Denmark. There the prince took a small room in a poor cottage near to his father's palace. The only furniture was a table, a bench and a bed, but the prince at once went out and bought an old spinning wheel together with some wool.

"There," he said. "Now I'm going to look for work. And as we can't have you sitting about doing nothing, you can spin this wool."

Time passed, and every evening the prince would return with a loaf of bread and some money, which he said he had earned by chopping wood up at the palace. The princess would go out to buy food, but most of the time she sat at the spinning wheel, working till her fingers ached.

Then one evening the prince brought home a load of pots and pans in a wheelbarrow. He had lacked the money to pay for them, he told his wife, and so she would have to go out and sell them for as much as she could get.

She was sitting in the street, and had sold only one or two of the things, when some riders came galloping by, and, as they passed her, one of the horses shied and, plunging among her pots and pans, broke them

all to pieces. The man rode off, and the poor princess went into the cottage and wept.

"Now we *are* in a fix," the prince said when he came home that evening. "I told you they weren't paid for, and we've only enough money to keep us from starving as it is. There's no help for it; you must go out and beg."

Glad at least to escape a scolding, the poor princess did as she was told, and went begging from door to door. The money she got on the first day was not very much, but the prince comforted her by saying he had found work for her. There was to be a big wedding up at the palace, and a lot of baking and cooking had to be done. He had arranged for her to go there and help.

"And see that you put a little aside for me," he said.

"I can't steal," the princess replied.

"I didn't say 'steal'; I said 'put a little aside for me.' Have a jar under your petticoat and fill it when nobody's looking."

When the time came, he took her to the palace and left her in the kitchen, where she worked hard the whole day long. She succeeded in filling her jar with scraps of food, but just as she was leaving she was stopped by the cook, who took her by the shoulders and shook her till the food fell out from under her petticoat on to the floor.

"I knew it," said the cook. "I suppose you know I could get you sent to prison for this. However, I'll let you off this time, but don't let me see you here again."

The princess returned to the cottage in tears, but the prince told her not to worry, as he had found her better work to do. The next day, the seamstresses would be going to the palace to finish the wedding dress. The bride's arrival had been delayed, but as the princess was the same build and height she could go and be fitted for the dress in her place.

"And by the way," he said, "see that you bring a little of the material home with you, as it will always come in useful."

The princess burst into tears when she heard this, and begged her husband to excuse her, saying she could not bear to steal.

"Rubbish!" said the prince. "Do as I tell you!"

So the next day she went to the palace and tried on the wedding dress and other fineries. There was silk and satin, and there was wool and linen, enough and to spare, and she managed to hide a little of each in her bosom. But just as she was leaving, the head seamstress had her searched, and of course they found on her the stolen materials. So again the princess was harshly spoken to and told never to go there again.

The prince, however, comforted her as before, saying he had other work for her to do. The wedding had been fixed for the very next day, and the bride had still not arrived. But the ceremony would have to go on, and it had been decided that the person who had tried on the wedding dress should stand in for the bride.

This, the princess exclaimed, she could not do, as she had been ordered never to be seen in the palace again. All the prince could say to this, however, was that that was the king and his son's command, and they must be obeyed.

On the morning of the ceremony, the prince told his wife that she would have to go to the palace by herself, as he was not well and would stay in bed. So off she went, promising to return as soon as possible.

At the palace she was helped into the wedding dress with the veil and the train and the bridal wreath, and soon a splendid coach arrived, drawn by six milk-white horses, all with pink muzzles, and all shod with shoes of gold. The princess took her seat beside the handsome prince, and they drove off, followed by a grand procession of carriages.

On their way to the church they had to pass the little cottage that was the princess's home, and as they did so she saw, to her horror, that it was on fire.

"Stop! Stop!" she cried. "Oh, my poor Greylegs!"

"Now, what is all this about?" the bridegroom asked angrily.

"My poor husband!" she cried. "He's ill in bed, and now he'll be burnt to death! We must save him."

"Greylegs!" said the bridegroom. "Fiddlesticks." He'll be all right."

And plead as she would, he refused to stop for her and drove on straight to the church.

After the ceremony, they returned to the palace, passing the cottage again on the way. And now she saw that there was nothing left of it but the blackened, burnt-out walls.

Tearing off the wedding dress as she got out of the coach, she flung it on the ground together with the veil and the bridal wreath, crying that she could wait no longer but must find out what had become of Greylegs.

"Greylegs!" said the bridegroom. "We'll soon find out about him."

So saying, he went into the next room, and in a few minutes returned wearing the same old clothes that she knew so well. And at once she understood that her Greylegs was none other than the prince of Denmark whom she had despised.

"Well," he said, "you've got your beggarly prince, and you've done what you said you would sooner do than marry him: you've spun wool and you've sold pots and pans in the street and you've gone begging."

Yes, indeed, she had done all these things; and still she was more than happy to have married her beggarly prince.

And that is how the proud princess of England became the princess of Denmark, and in time its queen. Only, it is such a long time ago that nobody now living can remember anything at all about it.

Finding a wife

Once upon a time a young farm-hand, whose name was Hans, decided that it was time to find a wife. So he rode off in search of one.

Ahead of him as he rode he saw three farms; and he thought that in one or other of them he would surely find what he wanted.

At the first of them they had a daughter, and her name was Maren. She seemed to be just right for him, so he proposed to her.

Maren was so delighted at the thought of getting Hans for a husband that she went straight down to the cellar to draw off some beer with which to celebrate the occasion. She had just turned on the tap when an idea struck her.

"If I get married to Hans," she thought, "we shall have a baby. I wonder what sort of clothes I should buy for the baby?"

And she got so absorbed in thinking about this that she clean forgot about the beer and it flowed out all over the floor.

When Maren failed to return with the beer, her mother got impatient and went down to the cellar to find out what was going on.

"What's happened, Maren?" she asked.

"Well, Mother," Maren said, "I was just thinking that if I get married to Hans, we shall have a baby; and I was wondering what sort of clothes to buy for it."

"Why, yes, of course," her mother said; and she, too, stood and wondered, while the beer went on flowing from the tap.

Soon, Maren's father came down to see what was happening.

"What's going on?" he asked.

"Well, you see," said his wife, "we were just thinking that if Maren marries Hans they'll have a baby, and we were wondering what sort of clothes to buy for it."

"Why, yes, of course," said her husband; and he, too, stood wondering, as the beer went on flowing from the tap and soon was washing round their ankles.

At last Hans came down himself to see what was going on.

"You see," Maren's father said, "we were just thinking that if Maren marries you, she'll have a baby, and we wondered what sort of clothes to buy for it."

Hans now thought he had enough of this foolish family, so he rode on to the next farm.

There he found the farmer up on the roof, pulling off the thatching.

"What on earth are you doing that for?" asked Hans.

"Well, you see," said the man, "I have a son but he's been missing now for over a year; and as we were thatching the house when he disappeared, I thought he might have got lost underneath it."

"They get worse," thought Hans; and so he rode

on to the third farm, where he found the farmer up a tree, chopping off a branch.

Now, this farmer was hard of hearing, but disliked people to know about it. He had therefore worked out the questions he expected people to ask him, and had all the answers ready.

The first thing anybody would ask him today, he supposed, would be why he was chopping the branch off. Next, what length of wood he would need for the job. Then what his horses were like (because usually his visitors were horse dealers); and lastly, which was the way to the village.

Hans had now arrived at the tree. "Hello, there!" he said.

"For an axe head," the farmer replied.

"You can stick that down your throat," retorted Hans.

"As far as this knot," said the farmer.

"How are your daughters?" asked Hans.

"They're both with foal," answered the farmer.

"Oh, go and hang yourself," said Hans.

"Between those two trees," answered the man.

"It's no use," thought Hans to himself. "They are all getting more and more mad." So he rode back to the first farm and in time married Maren after all.

South of the sun and east of the moon

A poor cottager was gathering fuel in the forest when he met a mysterious stranger. Though he did not know it, the stranger was the Devil in disguise and he wanted to tempt the poor man. Pretending to be sorry for him, he promised to help him out of his poverty. If he would give him something that was in his cottage that he knew nothing about, he should have all the money he and his wife needed to keep them for the rest of their lives. The poor man could think of nothing in his cottage that he knew nothing about and so he readily agreed.

"Now," said the stranger, "what I want is the child that your wife is bearing. It will be a boy; and when he is seventeen years old, you must bring him here and give him to me, as you have promised."

The poor man was sad at heart when he learnt that he had promised to give away his wife's child which he had known nothing about. But a promise is a promise; and he went off home to his cottage where from now on he and his wife had all the money they wanted.

Their child grew into an exceptionally clever boy who taught himself both to read and to write and indeed became very studious and learned.

Now on the boy's sixteenth birthday, a year before it was time for the poor man to give his child up to the Devil, he took the boy aside and told him about the terrible promise he had made.

"Don't worry, Father," said the boy. "I was told about your promise in a dream last night. A beautiful girl appeared to me, in a wonderful palace south of the sun and east of the moon. She told me what I must do. First of all, you must take a knife and make me a three-legged stool and table, and see that they are finished before the year is out."

This the father did, and at length, when the time came round for the boy to be handed over to the stranger, father and son went off together into the forest. Once there, the boy drew a circle round his father, saying that he was to stay inside it when the Devil came to claim him. Then he drew another circle and sat down inside it at his table.

It was not long before the Devil appeared to claim the boy but, being unable to cross the circle, he could not get him. Nor, try as he may, could he get at the boy's father. There he was, running backwards and forwards between the two circles until in the end he gave up and went off. But as he went, he cursed them both and said: "The father can go home after a day and a night, but the boy will stay in his circle for the rest of his life."

And so he disappeared, leaving the poor man almost in despair again. But the boy called to him and said: "Don't worry, Father, because the beautiful girl in my dream said she would come and rescue me and that she would be my bride. You can go home and tell my mother that I will be quite safe and all will be well."

The father left after a night and a day, looking back sadly at his son still trapped in the circle. But he believed that the boy would be rescued in time.

Days passed and the boy waited for his rescuer to come. He had to wait for many days because the palace of this beautiful girl, who was a princess, was a long way off, south of the sun and east of the moon, and in the middle of the wind. But she travelled all that way to find him and free him. She then took the boy with her to her palace where they were betrothed and lived very happily together.

But then one day, the boy said he yearned to see his father and mother again, it was so long since he had left home. The princess told him that she would gladly take him home and that he could stay there all the time he wanted. She would give him a ring and when he should long to return to the palace and to his life with her, he should turn the ring on his finger and make the wish. But he must never use the ring to wish for her to come to him because, if he did so, he would never see her again.

Taking the ring that she offered him from her finger, the boy promised to do exactly as she said. The princess then took the boy home. The boy's parents were of course delighted to see him because they had thought they would never set eyes on him again, and the family spent a joyful time together.

In time, however, he longed to see the beautiful princess again; and forgetting all that she had told him, he went outside the house, and, turning the ring on his finger, wished for her to come for him. In a twinkling she was there, and, taking the ring, gave him a slap on the face and vanished, leaving him to reflect on his broken promise and to mourn that he would never see her again. And he could not go on living with his father and mother. For what was there to do in their house but read and write; and you can't go on doing that all the time.

Now, one day he happened to go out into the forest, and there he heard two people quarrelling. When he asked them why they were quarrelling, they told him it was over a pair of slippers. For every step that you took when you had those slippers on, you travelled ten miles. The boy then asked to try them and no sooner had he got them on than he took one step and was ten miles away, leaving the two still quarrelling.

Walking fast all day long, he arrived that evening at the palace of the king of the fishes and he asked the king if he knew where to find the princess who lived in the palace south of the sun, east of the moon and in the middle of the wind.

The king did not know, but said that if he would wait until later that evening when the fishes came home to rest by the shore, he would send his footman to ask if any of them knew where the palace lay. The king was as good as his word but none of the fishes, not even the oldest among them, knew where to find the palace that lay south of the sun, east of the moon and in the middle of the wind. The king of the fishes, however, had a brother who was king of the birds, and he thought he might know where to find the palace. "I will write him a letter," he said, "and you can take it to him."

So the next morning the boy set out on his journey with the letter; and since for every step that he took he travelled ten miles, he arrived at the palace of the king of the birds that same evening. When the king

had read the letter, he said that he did not know
where the palace was, but if the boy would wait a
little longer, till the birds came home to roost, he
would send his footman to ask if any of them knew.
But none of them knew the way to the palace south
of the sun, east of the moon and in the middle of the
wind. They asked him to wait a little longer, till the
two oldest of the crows arrived home; but they did
not know either.

The king of the birds then told the boy that he had
another brother, who was king of the winds. He might

be able to say where the palace lay. "I will write him a letter," he said, "and you can take it to him."

The next morning the boy set out with the letter; and travelling at the same speed of ten miles for every step, he arrived at the palace of the king of the winds that same evening. The king said, when he had read the letter, that he did not know where the palace lay; but if the boy would wait a little longer, till the north-west wind came home to rest, he would send his footman to ask if he knew. Well, the north-west wind said he knew where the palace was, but he could not take anyone with him on foot, as that would hold him up on his way.

Both the boy and the king were glad to hear that someone knew the way to the palace, and the king sent word back to the nor'-wester that he would have to take the boy with him, no matter how slowly he walked, because the boy had been so good and had brought him letters from his two brothers, whom he had not seen for many a long day. And of course the nor'-wester had to obey the king's command.

So the next morning the boy and the wind set out together, the wind at first moving very, very slowly so as not to get too far ahead. But as the boy went ten miles at every step, the nor'-wester found itself having to hurry in order to keep up with him. In the end it had to whip itself up into a regular gale so as not to get left behind.

By noon, the two had reached the gate of the palace south of the sun, east of the moon and in the middle of the wind; and the nor'-wester now blew away on its own business, while the boy took off his magic slippers, so as not to go past the palace, and walked on in his stockinged feet. The princess sat there inside; and she was overjoyed to see him again, for she had thought that he would never be able to reach her.

The boy and the beautiful princess now held a magnificent feast to celebrate his return. They still live happily together as man and wife, in the palace south of the sun, east of the moon and in the middle of the wind.

A sledge ride

A rich farmer in Jutland had an only daughter who was very beautiful, but who at the same time was inclined to be melancholy. No one ever saw her smile, and as she sat alone in her room for hours on end she soon grew pale and thin. Though her father did what he could to cheer her up, it was all of no use; she remained as unhappy as ever, and he began to fear that the poor girl would die.

One day, in a last effort to cure her, he announced that the man who succeeded in making her laugh should have her for his wife and should also inherit the mansion when he died. Needless to say, this tempting offer brought many men to his house, eager to try their luck; but all in vain.

In time, the news of the unhappy girl and her father's offer came to the ears of a farm boy whose name was Saucy Jack, as one might say. At once he set off for the mansion, to see what he could do.

He had not gone far when he met an old woman, who asked him where he was going and what his errand was; and when he told her, she said: "Have you any particular plan for making the girl laugh?"

"Not really," Jack replied, "but I expect I shall think of one when I get there."

"That may be harder than you suppose," said the woman. "So let me help you."

So saying, she brought out a sledge, on the back of which was carved a small bird.

"Now this," she said, "is a magic sledge, which will go all by itself. Just sit down on it and say, 'Chirrup, little dicky-bird,' and it will start off and won't stop again till you tell it to. If anybody touches it, the bird will say 'Chirrup!' and if you then cry 'Hold tight!' they will have to hold on behind and run after you till you release them. Now look after it, and I think that sledge will help you."

After thanking the old woman for her handsome present, Jack at once sat down on it. Then, "Chirrup, little dicky-bird!" he said; and off it sped, as if drawn by invisible horses. Everyone who saw it had to stop and stare at this wonderful sledge that could go all by itself.

Late that evening Jack arrived at an inn, where he put up for the night, taking his magic sledge for greater safety into his bedroom.

Everybody at the inn had seen his swift arrival and all were curious to have a peep at the sledge, though none so curious as the three servant girls, who were dying to see it. So when they thought that Jack must be fast asleep, they all crept into his room to have a really good look at it. They inspected it from one side and they inspected it from the other, and then they touched it.

"Chirrup!" said the little bird all of a sudden. "Hold tight!" cried Jack, who of course had been watching the girls. So there they stood, all three of them; and try as they would, they could not escape.

41

Early the next morning Jack got up and, pretending not to see the unfortunate girls who were holding it, sat on his sledge and started off again on his journey; and of course the poor girls had to run behind.

They had not travelled far when they came to a forge. The blacksmith had just got up; and looking out of his cottage window, he saw the sledge with Jack sitting on it and the three screaming girls running after it.

His first thought was that the girls were chasing Jack, and so he seized the third girl with the idea of stopping her.

"Chirrup!" said the bird at once. "Hold tight!" cried Jack. And so the blacksmith was caught like the girls and had to run along after them.

Soon they came to a village, where the bells were ringing for service, and the clergyman and his curate were on their way to church. As the strange procession swung past, the clergyman felt sorry for the girls and the blacksmith holding on to the sledge and unable to get free, and so he grasped the blacksmith round the waist and tried to pull him away, the curate in turn seizing the clergyman's vestments.

"Chirrup!" said the bird. "Hold tight!" cried Jack. And so the clergyman and the curate were caught and had to run behind after the rest.

By this time they were not far from the rich farmer's house, and when they arrived there Jack turned in through the gates and careered three times round the courtyard. There was such a commotion, with Jack shouting "Hi!", the girls screaming, the blacksmith blustering, and the clergyman and his curate pleading to be released, that the entire household ran out to see what it was all about.

The farmer stood on the steps roaring with laughter

at this remarkable procession, and, turning to his daughter, who had come out and was standing beside him, he saw that she, too, was laughing; laughing so heartily that the tears were rolling down her cheeks.

"Stop!" cried Jack, and the sledge stopped instantly. "Let go!" he said; and the clergyman and his curate, the blacksmith and the three girls all hurried off home as fast as their legs would carry them.

As for Jack, he had cleared the steps at a single bound and stood at the daughter's side.

"You're cured!" he cried. "And now you shall be mine!"

And that's how Saucy Jack won the rich farmer's daughter. He always knew how to keep her amused, so that she never grew melancholy again; and when her father died, the happy couple succeeded to the mansion and all its lands.

The princess and the gold dancing shoes

A young man set out to seek his fortune and on the way he fell in with an old man, who asked him for alms. The young man said he had no money to give, but would gladly share with him the little food that he had.

Now, when they had eaten and were about to take leave of each other, the old man said: "You shared with me what you had, so now I want to give you this ball and this wand. They are both magic. When you hold the wand up before you, you will become invisible; and if you touch the ball with the wand, it will roll along in front of you, showing you which way to go."

Thanking the old man for his rare gift, and bidding him goodbye, the young man threw the ball on the ground and touched it with the wand as the stranger had told him.

The ball at once began to roll, and it kept on rolling in front of him until he arrived at a great city. There, a grim sight met his eyes. Stuck up on poles round the city walls were many heads of men who had been executed.

Asking the first person he met the reason for this, the young man was told that there was great unhappiness in the city because of the princess. Every night she wore out twelve pairs of gold dancing shoes, no-one knew how or why. The old king was so puzzled and upset by this he had promised that whoever succeeded in finding out how it happened should have the princess's hand in marriage. But whoever tried and failed would have his head cut off. The princess was very beautiful and so many men had tried, but every one of them had failed and had paid with his life.

On hearing of the king's offer, the young man thought he would try his luck; and so, going to the palace, he had himself presented before the king. Convinced that the young man would fail, and feeling very sorry for him, the king tried to discourage him from the enterprise. But when the young man said he was determined to try, the king explained that he had to sleep three nights in the princess's bedroom. If he had failed to discover anything by then, he would certainly have to be executed.

Nothing daunted, the young man was led on the first night into the princess's bedroom, where a couch had been prepared for him. Twelve new pairs of gold dancing shoes lay by the princess's bed. Placing his magic wand beside him, with his knapsack hanging from it, he lay down on the couch, resolved not to close an eye the whole night. Indeed, he managed to keep awake for quite a long time, during which nothing at all happened; but then, despite all his good intentions, he began to doze and at length fell fast asleep. When he awoke, it was broad daylight and the dancing shoes were all gone; and he could only hope to do better on the next night.

On the next night, however, the very same thing happened; and so now he had only a single night left.

On the third night he succeeded in keeping awake all the time and soon he heard a voice, asking the princess if he was asleep. The princess said that he was. The voice he had heard belonged to a maid, who was dressed all in white, and she then said that she would make sure. And taking a gold pin, she thrust it into the young man's heel. But he never even winced, and so the maid left him, with the pin still sticking in his heel.

Then what should they do next but push the princess's bed aside, revealing a trap-door and some steps. The young man lost no time in making himself invisible with his magic wand, and, after hiding the gold pin in his knapsack, he followed the princess and her maid as they descended the steps.

Before long they arrived at a forest, where the trees, the flowers and the grass were all of silver; and as they left the forest on the other side, the invisible young man broke off a small branch from one of the trees and put it in his knapsack.

"What was that?" exclaimed the princess, hearing the rustle of the leaves.

"It was only the wind in the trees," the maid said.

Continuing on their way they came to another forest, where the trees, the flowers and the grass were all of gold; and as they left it on the other side, the young man broke off another branch and put it in his knapsack.

"What was that?" exclaimed the princess.

"Only the wind," the maid said.

46

In time they came to another forest, where the trees, the flowers and the grass were all of diamonds; and as they left it on the other side, the young man broke off another branch and put it in his knapsack.

"What was that?" exclaimed the princess.

"Only the wind," the maid said.

Presently they arrived at a lake, and there the princess and her maid got into a boat, followed, of course, by the young man. The boat rocked when he got in it, but the maid said to the princess that it was only the wind blowing across the water.

Waiting for the princess on the other side of the lake was an ugly old troll, and he was grumbling because he said she was late. He then led her to his castle, and when they all arrived there he seated the princess at table in the banqueting hall, while the maid stood behind her on one side and the young man, still invisible, on the other.

After they had feasted, the troll led the princess in a dance. Together they danced twelve dances, and after each dance she threw her worn gold shoes into a corner, where the young man at once picked them up and put them in his knapsack.

When the dancing was over, the troll accompanied the princess back to the boat, and soon she, the maid and the young man were back on the other side. As soon as they had landed, the young man ran off as fast as his legs would carry him back to the palace, where he lay down on his couch, seeming to be fast asleep when the princess re-entered the room.

In the morning, when the young man was brought before the king again, he said he would like to tell him of a dream he had had during the night. He then told how he had seen the princess and her maid go down the stairs, after the maid had first thrust a gold pin into his heel to see if he was asleep.

"I think this was the pin," the young man said, holding it up for the king to see.

Next, he said, he had dreamt that they had passed through three forests, and that in the first of the forests the trees, the flowers and the grass had been all of silver, that in the second forest they had been all of gold, and in the third forest they had been all of diamonds.

"I then dreamt that we came to a lake, that we crossed the lake in a boat and that an ugly old troll took the princess into his castle where, after feasting in the hall, he danced twelve dances with her. After each dance the princess threw her worn-out gold shoes into a corner. And here they are."

The old king was very grieved when he heard about the ugly old troll and his daughter, but he was glad to know at last how the gold shoes came to be worn out, and he at once offered to carry out his part of the bargain and give the young man his daughter's hand in marriage.

First, however, the young man said he wished to visit the troll, and he asked the princess if she would lend him her gold thimble. With this in his knapsack he descended the steps and after passing through the three forests and crossing the lake arrived at the troll's castle. Stealing up to the troll, he thrust the gold pin he had taken from his heel into the troll's heart. Three drops of blood fell from his heart as the troll died, and these the young man caught in the princess's gold thimble.

Crossing the lake again, the young man arrived in the forest on the other side. There he poured a drop of blood from the thimble on to the ground, and

49

instantly the trees and the flowers and the grass that were all of diamonds were transformed into men, women and children. They had been bewitched by the wicked troll; and they were now so happy to have been released from his spell that they asked the young man to be their king, for the enchanted forest was indeed a kingdom.

They all then went with him till they came to the next forest. There the young man poured another drop of the troll's blood on to the ground, and instantly the trees and the flowers and the grass that were all of gold were transformed into people. They, too, asked the young man if he would be their king.

In the next forest the young man poured out the last drop of the troll's blood, and instantly the trees and the flowers and the grass that were of silver were transformed into people, and they also begged the young man to be their king.

The people of the three forests now accompanied the young man to the palace, where they told the old king of the troll's spell and of how the young man had released them. The princess's spell had also been broken now. So, amid great festivity, she married the young man who had freed her; and there was more rejoicing when the same young man, who could so miraculously make himself invisible, was crowned king of the three kingdoms whose people he had set free.

The hen that swallowed a nut

A cock and a hen went gathering nuts: the cock shook the nuts off the tree and the hen picked them up. But then the hen swallowed one of the nuts and it got stuck in her throat. So the cock ran off to the pond, and said: "Pond, give me water for my hen, who's in the forest and has a nut stuck in her throat."

But the pond would not give him water till he gave it silk. So off the cock ran to the housekeeper, and said: "Housekeeper, give me silk for pond; then pond will give me water for my hen, who's in the forest and has a nut stuck in her throat."

But the housekeeper would not give him silk till he gave her shoes. So off the cock ran to the shoemaker, and said: "Shoemaker, give me shoes for house-keeper; then housekeeper will give me silk for pond; then pond will give me water for my hen, who's in the forest and has a nut stuck in her throat."

But the shoemaker would not give him shoes till he gave him bristles. So off the cock ran to the boar, and said: "Boar, give me bristles for shoemaker; then shoemaker will give me shoes for housekeeper; then

51

housekeeper will give me silk for pond; then pond will give me water for my hen, who's in the forest and has a nut stuck in her throat."

But the boar would not give him bristles till he gave him corn. So off the cock ran to the thresher, and said: "Thresher, give me corn for boar; then boar will give me bristles for shoemaker, then shoemaker will give me shoes for housekeeper; then housekeeper will give me silk for pond; then pond will give me water for my hen, who's in the forest and has a nut stuck in her throat."

But the thresher would not give him corn till he gave him bread. So off the cock ran to the baker, and said: "Baker, give me bread for thresher; then thresher will give me corn for boar; then boar will give me bristles for shoemaker; then shoemaker will give me shoes for housekeeper; then housekeeper will give me silk for pond; then pond will give me water for my hen, who's in the forest and has a nut stuck in her throat."

But the baker would not give him bread till he gave him shovel. So off the cock ran to the carpenter, and said: "Carpenter, give me shovel for baker; then baker will give me bread for thresher; then thresher will give me corn for boar; then boar will give me bristles for shoemaker; then shoemaker will give me shoes for housekeeper; then housekeeper will give me silk for pond; then pond will give me water for my hen, who's in the forest and has a nut stuck in her throat."

But the carpenter would not give him shovel till he gave him axe. So off the cock ran to the blacksmith, and said: "Blacksmith, give me axe for carpenter; then carpenter will give me shovel for baker; then baker will give me bread for thresher; then thresher will give me corn for boar; then boar will give me bristles for shoemaker; then shoemaker will give me shoes for housekeeper; then housekeeper will give me silk for pond; then pond will give me water for my hen, who's in the forest and has a nut stuck in her throat."

But the blacksmith would not give him axe till he gave him fire. So off the cock ran to Hell, and there he got fire. Then off he ran with fire to blacksmith and got axe; then off with axe to carpenter and got shovel; then off with shovel to baker and got bread; then off with bread to thresher and got corn; then off with corn to boar and got bristles; then off with bristles to shoemaker and got shoes; then off with shoes to housekeeper and got silk; then off with silk to pond and got water; then off with water to forest; where he found that the hen had choked on the nut and was dead.

At this the cock got so furious that he exploded with rage; or, in the Danish saying, into flint. And that's why you find so much flint lying on the ground when you walk round the Danish countryside.

Alexander and the golden bird

The king of Denmark lay very ill and seemed likely to die. Although sound in mind, he could stir neither hand nor foot, and no doctor in all the land could find any cure for him.

Now, one day there arrived from a far distant land a learned stranger, who claimed that he had a cure for the king's illness, though it would take a long time to work. Among his travelling things he had a twig, which they were to graft on to an apple-tree in the king's orchard and then tend it carefully.

The king's friends followed the stranger's instructions, the grafting took well, and after three years the twig bore a single blossom. It was unlike any other apple blossom, for it shone like the purest gold. The sight of this wonderful blossom convinced the king's friends that a cure for his sickness had at last been found. When the blossom set fruit, and the fruit ripened and the king ate it, the stranger had said, he would recover his health and strength.

Summer came round and the blossom was looking its very best when, on Midsummer Night, it vanished; somebody must have picked it. The whole country was plunged into the deepest grief by this; but there was nothing to be done except wait for the tree to blossom again another year. In the meantime, they erected a high fence round the precious tree and its twig, so high that neither animals nor men could climb over it. And the royal gardener kept the key of the gate in his pocket night and day.

In spring, the tree budded and turned green again, and in time the twig put forth another blossom, which also glittered like gold. But, alas, on Midsummer Night this blossom vanished too, no-one knew how. Once more the palace and all the land went into mourning.

Autumn passed and then winter, and when spring returned the twig bore yet another golden blossom. Now, the king had three sons; and the eldest son said to his father that on Midsummer Night he would keep watch, so that nobody should steal the blossom this time. All night long he sat there under the apple-tree; yet when day dawned it was seen that the blossom had vanished as before.

The next year, the golden apple-tree, as everyone now called it, bore another blossom; and this time the king's second son said he would sit up and watch. So, on Midsummer Night he sat there under the tree till it was dawn; but again the blossom had vanished in the morning.

In the seventh year of the king's illness, the tree sprang once again into leaf and again bore a single golden blossom. This time the youngest of the princes promised to stay up and watch on Midsummer Night. But instead of sitting underneath the tree as the others had done, he climbed it and sat just beneath the blossom. Then, on the last stroke of midnight, he saw a strange sight. A bird came flying through the branches and plucked the blossom off with its beak.

55

At once Alexander – for that was the youngest brother's name – seized hold of its tail. But the bird slipped through his fingers, leaving him holding one of its feathers. And, as he hurried back home to tell about his strange adventure, he saw that the feather in his hand shone like gold.

Everyone now agreed that their best plan would be to send for the stranger who had given them the twig; and when they had told him what had befallen the golden blossom and showed him the feather of the bird that had stolen it on Midsummer Night, he said: "There is only one thing now that can restore the king to health and strength. If he can hear the golden bird sing, he will get well at once. But it lives in a palace a thousand miles from here, in the direction of the rising sun."

At once the eldest son said he would seek out the bird, though it meant travelling to the ends of the earth, and would bring it home, cost what it might. So, equipping himself well for the journey and taking with him a grand suite of knights and grooms and other attendants, as well as a plentiful supply of gold, he rode off in the direction of the rising sun; and he lived in style and entertained lavishly. Thus in time he arrived at a splendid city that was surrounded by wonderful gardens. The sun shone, the roses bloomed and the birds sang all the year round; and the city was full of beautiful women and delicious wines. In this city he settled down, living a life of luxury, and forgetting all about the bird he had set out to find.

Time passed, and as nothing was heard from the eldest son, the second prince said he would go in search of his brother and the golden bird. Like the eldest prince he equipped himself well for the journey

and, setting out in the direction of the rising sun, travelled from country to country and at last arrived at the same great city as his brother. Together with him, he lived there in luxury; and neither of them gave any thought to their sick father and the golden bird that was to cure him.

As time went on, and nothing was heard from either of the sons, the youngest prince resolved that he would join in the search; and although unwilling at first to part with his last remaining son, the king finally gave him permission. He wanted Alexander to equip himself like the others, but this Alexander refused to do, saying that a lot of attendants would only mean trouble and delay. And so he rode off all by himself, taking only as much money as he could carry, and travelling indeed much faster than his brothers, stopping nowhere for pleasure but pressing on till in time he arrived at the same splendid city as his brothers.

Those brothers happened to be taking part in a magnificent feast, where there was dancing and much revelry; and they invited Alexander to join them. This he would not do, and told them of his determination to find the golden bird that was to cure their father. If they would not join him in the search, they should return home to him. But his brothers said they were well enough where they were, and in any case their father was an old man and would soon be dead anyway.

So the two eldest brothers stayed behind in the city of pleasure while Alexander rode on towards the rising sun. Now the way no longer went through flowering fields and fragrant gardens but across deserts and wildernesses, over lofty mountains and deep rivers, and through perilous bogs and swamps. Yet Alexander kept on, riding steadily towards the rising sun. But then a sad accident befell him; the horse that had borne him so well and faithfully this long way sank into a bog and was drowned, and Alexander very nearly drowned with it. From now on he had to make his way on foot.

As he was trudging along one day, he met a fox; and when Alexander told the fox about his quest for the golden bird that would cure his father's sickness, the fox offered to help him. "Get on my back," it said, "hold on to my ears. It will be a long journey and a rough one, and we've got to hurry."

Alexander did as the fox had said, and off it ran, going straight into a dark and gloomy forest where the sun never penetrated; and although Alexander ducked his head, he got torn and scratched by the thorns and briars till he bled. But he held on tightly, and late that evening they arrived safely on the other side.

"Stand on my back," said the fox, "and tell me what you see."

"I see a star in the east," said Alexander.

"That's the palace of the golden bird," said the fox. "Now, do what I tell you. At the palace I shall cast a spell on everything in it and around it. Pluck a hair out of my tail and hold it in front of you, and you'll find that every gate and door of the palace will open of its own accord. Go up the palace stairs, and, in the topmost room, you'll find the bird you are looking for, asleep in its golden cage. Take it out of the cage, put it in a wooden cage that stands next to it, and come straight back to me with it."

Soon they had arrived at the palace, which was a really gorgeous one, roofed all over with gold and glistening and sparkling in the rays of the sun. Pulling out a hair from the fox's tail, Alexander found as he approached the gates that all the guards lay fast asleep under the fox's spell, and at once the gates sprang open of their own accord, just as the fox had said. Every door he came to on his way upstairs also opened of its own accord when he held the hair from the fox's tail in front of him; and so he arrived at the topmost room, where, exactly as the fox had said, he found the bird asleep in a golden cage, set with pearls and precious stones. Opening the cage, Alexander took out the sleeping bird and put it in the wooden cage as he had been instructed. But when he looked at the bird again, he found that it had lost all its golden lustre and now was as dull as a sparrow. Thinking that something must surely have gone wrong, he put the bird back into its golden cage and at once it shone like gold again. Then picking up the cage with the bird in it, he made for the door. But now the spell had been broken; the bird uttered a piercing shriek which woke all the guards, who surrounding Alexander carried him off to the palace dungeons. There he was chained up and the door was barred and bolted. All alone in the dark, Alexander had plenty of time to reflect on how he had disobeyed his instructions.

All of a sudden, something stirred at his feet. It was the fox, which had burrowed its way through the ground till it had found him. Begging the fox's forgiveness, Alexander pleaded with it to help him out of his trouble for the sake of his sick father.

"You're a nice one for carrying out instructions, aren't you!" the fox said. "But never mind, I'll give you another chance. When they come for you at daybreak tomorrow, tell them that if they will give you the golden bird you will bring them the golden foal that is kept in the stables of the magician king far away from here, and they will agree to the bargain."

It all happened as the fox had said. When the guards came to fetch Alexander at dawn the next day, and he promised to bring them the golden foal if they would give him the golden bird, they at once agreed. And so Alexander was released. Hurrying to the fox at the palace gates, he jumped on its back, and soon they were racing off again through forest and thicket.

In the evening, when they had come through to the other side, the fox told Alexander to stand on its back and tell it what he saw; and Alexander said he could see the moon, shining straight in front of him.

"That's the palace of the magician king," said the

fox. "The roof is of copper. Now we shall be there in no time. Do as I tell you. I shall cast a spell on everything inside and about the palace, and with the help of a hair from my tail the gates and doors will fly open of their own accord. The stable is in the yard on the right, and you will find the golden foal standing in its box, which is all of silver. Every other hair of its mane and tail is of silver, and the rest are of gold. The saddle is of silver, and the bridle is of gold set with precious stones. Hanging beside the box you will find an ordinary horse-blanket and a plain halter of tow. Take the precious saddle and bridle off the foal and put the blanket and halter on it instead. Then lead the foal out to me."

Exactly as the fox had said, Alexander found the golden foal standing in its box; and a more beautiful animal, as it glittered there in the sun, could scarcely be imagined.

The magnificent saddle and bridle seemed to match the horse so well that Alexander did not have the heart to take them off; and as they were so near to the palace gates, he thought he could easily get into the saddle and be off before anybody could stop him. So, taking the foal by the bridle, he led it out of its box.

Scarcely were they outside the stable door, however, when the foal gave a loud whinny that could be heard all over the palace, and instantly the palace gates were shut and a crowd of giants, appearing from all directions at once, dragged poor Alexander off before the king. The punishment for attempting to steal the golden foal was death by slow torture, but the king decided to give Alexander a chance to save his life and at the same time win the golden foal and its harness. "Bring me," he said, "the fair Helen,

whom I have long wanted to possess, and you shall
have them."

When Alexander had agreed to perform the task,
and solemnly promised to return and give himself up
should he fail to complete it, he was at once released;
and returning to the palace gate, found the fox waiting
for him there. The fox was so angry that Alexander
was afraid it was going to devour him, so he hastened
to tell it what the king of the giants had made him
promise.

"That," said the fox, "is the most dangerous adventure of them all. And it's not a bit of use trying to go
through with it, because you never keep your word."

But when Alexander promised this time to do
everything exactly as it told him, the fox at last consented to help once more. So Alexander got up on
the fox's back again, and they sped off through forests
and across country, Alexander holding on to the fox's
ears for dear life.

When they came out of the forest that evening, the
fox told Alexander to stand up on its back and tell
what he saw.

"I see the sun rising in the east," said Alexander.

"No," said the fox, "that is the palace of the fair Helen, and it is surrounded on every side by tongues of fire. Inside the ring of flames is a lofty wall built of steel, and guarding the only gate in this wall are two bears. Inside that wall is another wall, and the gate is guarded by two lions. Inside that one is a third wall, and the gate is guarded by two dragons. Then, inside all the walls, stands the palace where, lying on a couch in a room on the topmost floor, is the fair Helen, who is attended by seven maidens. She is the most beautiful woman in the world; but she is kept closely guarded so that no man may ever have her for his wife. I shall cast a spell on her maids, as well as the dragons, the lions and the bears, but only for a quarter of an hour; and I cannot put out the flames, only dampen them down. You must go straight on through the raging fire, through the three gates in the three walls, and into the palace and up the stairs. Next you must take off the golden crown that the fair Helen will be wearing and place it on the couch; and then you must take her in your arms and, wrapping her long veil tightly round her to protect her from the flames, bring her straight here to me. Now pluck a hair from my tail to open the gates with. Fail me this time and we shall both be lost."

Well, Alexander ran through the raging flames as he had been instructed and, though they blistered his hands and feet, and scorched his hair, he kept straight on, past the bears and the lions and the dragons, all of which lay under a spell, until he came to the palace, where he ascended the stairs to the room where the fair Helen lay attended by her seven maids.

The sight of such beauty made Alexander's head swim, but he took the gold crown from the fair Helen's head and laid it on the couch beside her. As he did so, however, he very nearly gave up the adventure, for all at once the beautiful woman was gone, and in her place was an ugly old hag. But remembering his promise, he took her in his arms and, gathering her veil about her, ran down the stairs.

On he ran, through the gates guarded by the dragons and the lions and the bears, and through the scorching flames back to the fox. It was there waiting for him, and jumping on to its back with his burden he clung tightly to the fox's ears as they hurried off at top speed over hill and dale and through forests and across moors till, in the evening, they arrived at the palace of the magician king. On this breathtaking journey there had been no time for talking, and mostly Alexander had kept his eyes shut; but one thing he did see, and that was that, at the moment they passed through the flames, the woman he was holding had been restored to all her beauty and she was once more the fair Helen.

"Now," said the fox, "go in to the magician king, and when he sees you he will be very happy, and will want to marry Helen straight away. There will be a great feast, and Helen will be given the seat of honour. Before the feast is over, you, Alexander, must say you wish to leave, and will ask for the golden foal to be brought to you; and when you are seated in the saddle, Helen will bring you a stirrup cup – a glass of wine to cheer you on your way. As she hands it to you, you must seize her by the waist and lift her up on the foal, saying as you do so: 'Rise, golden foal, rise!' It will then ascend into the air and carry you out of sight; and all you have to do, an hour later, is to say 'Down, golden foal!' and it will descend to the ground, where I shall be waiting to receive you."

All went off as the fox had foretold. The magician king was so delighted to see the fair Helen that he ordered a great feast to be prepared, and seated Helen in the place of honour at his side. Then, when the feast was nearly at an end, Alexander said that he must leave, and the golden foal was brought out, all ready harnessed and saddled. Alexander leapt into the saddle, Helen brought him the stirrup cup, and he seized her by the waist and lifted her up in front of him. "Rise, golden foal, rise!" he cried; and it rose straight into the air and was lost to view in the clouds. An hour went by, and Alexander said: "Down, golden foal!" and soon they were back on earth, where the fox was waiting to welcome them.

After riding all through the night with the fox as their guide, Alexander and Helen arrived at the palace with the golden roof that was the home of the golden bird.

When Alexander rode into the palace courtyard on the gorgeous golden foal, with the fair Helen mounted in front of him, everyone, including the king, turned out to greet them. The king invited them into the palace, but Alexander refused to dismount until the bird had been brought to him in its cage. When they brought it, the golden bird at once began to sing, and its song was sweeter than any Alexander had ever heard before. All who heard it rejoiced at its purity.

When Alexander had the golden bird and the cage in his hands, he cried instantly: "Rise, golden foal, rise!" and the foal rose straight into the air and was lost to view. Then, after an hour, he cried: "Down, golden foal!" and they descended to the ground where, once again, the fox was waiting to receive them.

The time had now come for them to part, the fox said, as Alexander by now had got everything he wanted. But he promised to come for the wedding, and then Alexander must help him in his turn, which Alexander gratefully promised to do.

"One more piece of advice before I go, though," said the fox; "never buy gallows-birds. Remember that."

And so they parted, the fox staying behind in the forest, while Alexander rode off with the fair Helen on the golden foal, holding in his hand the golden bird in its golden cage; and the bird sang sweetly for them all the way.

Travelling faster now than he had done on the way out, Alexander and the fair Helen soon arrived at the splendid city where his brothers lived. Outside the walls they met a procession, which was winding its way to the city gallows. Two criminals were going to be hanged, and a vast crowd followed them and the hangman. Stopping to watch the procession, Alexander saw to his horror that the condemned criminals were none other than his own brothers. After squandering all their money in drinking and making merry they had taken to cheating and stealing, and it was for those crimes that they were to be hanged.

Full of pity for his worthless brothers, Alexander asked what it would cost to purchase their freedom, and was told that they could go free if everybody they had robbed and cheated was repaid and the judge, the judge's clerk and the hangman and his assistant were paid for their trouble. That was a lot of money, but Alexander still had the gold he had set out with, so with this he purchased his brothers' freedom and they returned to the city together. There they put up at an inn, and Alexander told his brothers all about his adventures and how he had found the golden bird that was to cure their father by its singing. The next morning they set off for home, the two brothers on horses Alexander had bought for them.

One day, when they were all resting after a meal, the two brothers, who were envious of Alexander's success, put a sleeping draught in his cup and Helen's, so they both fell into a deep sleep. The two wicked men then carried their brother off and, tying a heavy stone round his neck, flung him into a pool.

Helen, when she awoke, was grief-stricken to find that Alexander was no longer with them; and the brothers, after pretending to look for him, said he must have been carried off by wild beasts. Helen was to go home with them, and they made her promise to tell their father that they had found the golden bird and had won both the fair Helen and the golden foal. So, taking the golden bird in its cage, she rode off with the brothers on the golden foal, shedding bitter tears at the loss of Alexander.

The king was neither better nor worse than when they had left him, and was overjoyed to see his two long-lost sons again. When they told him they had brought the golden bird that was to cure him by its singing, and that they had also brought the golden foal and the fair Helen, he praised their skill and bravery, as well as the love they had shown to him.

The golden bird was then brought in to the sick king's bedroom; but alas, it remained silent in its cage and would not sing a single note. Next the fair Helen came into the room. While kissing the king's hand, she, too, was silent, answering all the king's questions only with tears. Though they gave her a grand suite of rooms in the palace, she spent all her time weeping in the gallery outside. As for the golden foal, it would neither eat nor drink, nor would it allow anyone to enter its box. There was no joy at all in the palace.

Now, when Alexander was thrown into the pool, his friend the fox had been hiding close by; and no sooner were the wicked brothers out of sight than he had got him hauled out on to the bank. Alexander himself knew nothing of what had been done to him, but the fox soon told him.

"I warned you not to buy gallows-birds," it said. "You have only yourself to blame. And you can look after yourself in future."

But when Alexander begged the fox to help him just once more, saying how deeply sorry he was for his disobedience, the fox in the end agreed to do so. But he was to find his own way home. When he got there he was to pretend that he was a horse doctor, and all would be well. The golden foal would be cured at the sight of him, his father would recover, and he, Alexander, would marry the fair Helen. But before the wedding feast he was to go outside the palace on its eastern side, where the fox would be waiting to give him his final instructions.

After days of walking, Alexander at length arrived home; and meeting the master of the king's horse whom he knew well but who did not recognize him, was told that there was indeed a horse which needed attention, a splendid foal the two princes had brought home with them. It would neither eat nor drink, and kicked and bit everybody who approached it.

When Alexander went into its box, however, it neither kicked nor bit him, but whinnied with pleasure and ate peacefully out of his hand. It was now fully recovered, as everyone could see.

"As you are such a magician," said the master of the king's horse, "maybe you can cure another creature the princes brought home with them. The golden bird which was to cure the king by its singing, and which they endured many hardships in order to find, will not sing; it must be ill, too."

Well, no sooner did the golden bird hear Alexander's footsteps than it began to hop about in its cage, and within minutes it was singing happily away as it had not done for many a long day. And when the fair Helen heard it, she came running into the room to find out what had caused it. On seeing Alexander there, she at once fell into his arms and embraced him.

So now the whole truth came out. The wicked brothers were thrown into the palace dungeons, where they would do no more harm. The king was restored to health and strength at once. And it was announced that Alexander himself was to marry the fair Helen.

Having now learnt his lesson, Alexander this time was careful to carry out the fox's instructions; and going outside the palace on the eastern side, he found his friend there waiting for him.

"Now," said the fox, "It's your turn to help me. Draw your sword and cut off my head and my tail. Then put my head where my tail is now, and my tail where my head is."

This, Alexander said, he could not do to a friend who had been so good to him. But the fox reminded him of his solemn promise, telling him that if he failed this time he would find himself back in the pool the fox had saved him from. So, sorrowfully, Alexander drew his sword and did as the fox had instructed him.

He had no sooner done so than the fox had vanished, and in its place stood an old man, who was dressed just like a king. Together they returned to the palace, where Alexander's father at once recognized his companion as his long-lost older brother. He indeed was the rightful king, but his mother, because she wanted her favourite younger son to reign, had had the older boy taken and left in the forest to be cared for by an old woman who was a witch. It was the old woman who, in a fit of anger one day, had turned the boy into a fox.

The king now offered to renounce his throne altogether, but his brother said: "Let me be king just for tonight; and let your son succeed me tomorrow. Then for as long as we live, we two old men can continue to give him the help and counsel that he needs."

The king readily agreed to this wise suggestion; and so the next day Alexander was proclaimed king and also married the fair Helen. The old king and his brother who had been bewitched lived on for many years yet; and together they gave Alexander so much help and good counsel that he grew into the wisest king in all the world. The golden bird sang happily for them all; and whoever listened to its song knew neither sorrow nor sickness.

The men of Mols

I

In the part of Jutland called Mols, whose inhabitants have long been famous for their lack of brains, a party of men were out walking one day when they saw a tree that was overhanging a pond. They were rather puzzled by this, but then in their wisdom they concluded that the tree was thirsty and trying to reach the water. So they agreed to help it.

This was not so easy, because the branches were too high up for them to reach them and pull them down. Then one of them had an idea. He would climb the tree, and if one of the others held on to his legs, a third on to *his* legs, and so on, they would be able to haul the branches down like a rope.

They at once set about doing this. But when they were all clinging to one another and the branches were beginning to bend, the hands of the topmost man who was holding them began to smart, and he shouted to the others: "Stop a bit, while I spit on my hands."

He then let slip with both hands in order to spit on them, and the whole party fell with a plop into the pond.

II

A stork had the bad habit when searching for frogs of walking through the village field and treading down the corn; so the men of Mols held a meeting to decide how they should deal with the nuisance. It was suggested that the village herdsman should be engaged to chase the stork out of the corn, but then it was decided that, as he had very big feet, he would do more harm than the stork.

One of the assembled men then had a brilliant idea. So that the herdsman should not trample down the corn he proposed that they should carry him through the field, and this they then proceeded to do. Taking the field gate off its hinges, they seated the man on top of it, and then eight of the villagers carried him through the cornfield. Thus the herdsman was able to drive the stork out of the field without trampling down the corn.

Never say "never"

A fisherman lived with his wife in a little cottage by the sea-shore, and they were so poor that they had no other possessions but children; but of those they had plenty, and more kept on coming. Nearby there lived a grocer and his wife. They had no children, and because of that were very unhappy.

Now, when the fisherman's wife gave birth to yet another son, the grocer said with a sigh, as he offered his congratulations: "A son is just what we could do with."

"A daughter would do just as well," his wife retorted.

"Well," he said, "anything would be better than nothing. But let's make a bargain," he proposed to the fisherman. "If, one day, we should get a daughter, then she shall marry your son. That would be a good catch, now, wouldn't it?"

"Shall we put it in writing?" suggested the fisherman.

"Yes, let's do that," said the grocer. And he chalked it up on one of the house beams.

Well, over the years the grocer and his wife became very rich and, to add to their joy, they did in time get a daughter and were delighted that life had given them all they wanted. But they forgot all about the writing on the beam.

Now, as the daughter grew up, she and the fisherman's son began to play together. They used to play all day long on the shore and in the woods. But it so happened that one day they fell out and the girl angrily told the boy she was not going to be his friend any longer.

"Ah, but you are going to be my wife," the fisherman's son replied. "Because it's written up on the beam".

This the girl refused to believe, though when she got home she asked her mother.

"Well," said her mother, "there was some talk about that."

"Yes," her father agreed, "so there was. But you will never, never marry a poor fisherman's son."

Yet as the children grew up they grew more and more fond of each other, and they promised that they would always remain true to each other. One day, the girl took a gold ring from her finger, broke it in two and gave one half to the fisherman's son as a token of their betrothal.

Meanwhile, however, the grocer had seen the way things were going, and made up his mind to be rid of the fisherman's boy. Shortly afterwards a ship arrived from England and the grocer wrote a letter to the captain which he cunningly got the fisherman's son to deliver. The letter asked the captain to take the boy away with him, to somewhere so far distant that he would never be able to get home again. So the captain kept the boy on board his ship and sailed off with him, while the grocer's daughter wept and mourned but kept on hoping for his return.

At length the ship arrived in England; but although the captain and his crew went ashore every day, the poor boy was kept a prisoner on board. One day when he had been left all by himself, he took a look over the ship's side and there, in the water, he saw two cats, one grey and one white, fighting each other. When it looked as if the little white one was going to be killed, the boy took a boathook and pushed the grey one under the water so that it was drowned. The little white cat swam down under the ship and, a moment later, up rose a beautiful mermaid who said: "Fisherman's boy, come down here to me and get your reward."

Without waiting to be asked twice, the boy dived overboard and the mermaid caught him in her arms and led him down to the bottom.

As they walked down there, the mermaid told the fisherman's son that the white cat whom he had saved was her husband, and the grey one he had killed had been the wicked sea-troll. And so in time they came to a house.

"That's the house of my youngest sister," the mermaid said. "Go in and tell her what you have done and she'll give you her hymn book with a silver clasp. It will come in useful."

Well, doing as she said, the boy soon came out with the hymn book in his hand, and they walked on till they came to another little house.

"That's the house of my next sister," said the mermaid. "Go in and ask her for her scissors. They'll come in useful."

Going on their way, they came to a third little house.

"That's the house of my eldest sister," said the mermaid. "Go in and get her old sack."

Soon they came to yet another house.

"That's the house of my mother," said the mermaid. "Go in and tell her what you have done and she will give you her old fiddle."

Soon they came to yet another house.

"That's the house of my grandmother," said the mermaid. "She has the best thing of all – a sword. Tell her what you've done, and she'll give it to you. It will come in useful."

When the fisherman's son had returned with the

sword, the mermaid explained to him the uses of the five things he had got. If somebody was ill and about to die, he was to read a few verses from the hymn book and that person would get well again. By simply clipping the scissors in the air he would be able to make himself as many clothes as he wanted, all ready to wear. From the old sack he could shake all the food he wanted. If he played the fiddle, everybody would start to dance, and would keep on dancing till he stopped. But the sword was his best possession, because he had only to swing it three times above his head and everyone facing him, even a whole army, would be turned to stone. And by swinging it three times in the opposite direction he would be able to bring them all to life again.

The fisherman's son had hardly finished thanking the mermaid for all her kindness when, lo and behold, he was back on board the ship again.

Of course he could hardly wait to try out the marvellous gifts he had received, and especially the fiddle, because he had always wanted a fiddle. Hardly had he touched the strings with the bow when at once it started to play, all of itself.

Now, the king of England had a large garden that ran down to the shore where the ship lay at anchor, and it so happened that the king was walking in the garden when he heard the fiddle. Like it or not, he had to dance; and as the fisherman's son kept on playing, the king was nearly danced off his feet.

Later that evening when the fiddling had stopped, the king sent word to find out who the fiddler was and to command him, on pain of death, to come to the palace. The terrified captain could only say that there had been nobody on board at the time except for the ship's boy.

"Then send him," said the king.

So off went the fisherman's boy, taking his fiddle with him. But on seeing him, the king refused to believe that he was the fiddler and had him thrown into gaol.

"Hold on a minute," said the boy. "We'll have a little dance first." And taking up his fiddle he began to play, and the king and all his court had to dance. The king begged and pleaded with him to stop, telling him he was free to go; and so the boy returned to his ship.

A few days later the ship weighed anchor and they sailed for Spain. Things in that country were in a very bad state because the emperor of Turkey had conquered most of the land, and the king lay dying from a wound received in the fighting.

The fisherman's boy was successful in escaping from the ship this time, and going to the palace he asked for an audience with the king. There could be no question of that, he was told, and if he did not take himself off at once they would set the dogs on him. But the boy just took up his fiddle and began to play; and everybody, from the palace guard to the kitchen-maid, had to dance. To get him to stop, they agreed to let him see the king.

The poor king lay in his bed, but no sooner had the boy read just a single verse from his hymn book with the silver clasp than he began to move first his hands and then his feet. When the boy had read a second verse, he was able to sit up; and when he had read a third verse, the king got out of bed and was fully recovered. Naturally, the king was very grateful, and asked the boy what reward he could give him. The boy wanted no other reward, he said, than to be allowed to accompany the king in his war against the Turks, and to this the king gladly gave his permission. Only he must first get himself a uniform. No sooner said than done; the boy had only to get out his scissors and make a few clips in the air, and in a trice he had the grandest of uniforms to put on.

The war was going badly and the soldiers had hardly anything to eat. But the fisherman's son, now wearing his splendid new uniform, had no sooner shaken his sack than out fell all the food that they needed. The war continued to go against them so, one evening, the boy just marched across to the Turkish lines and, swinging his sword three times over his head, turned the whole army into stone. There sat the Turkish emperor in his tent, unable to move, though splendid in silver and gold; and changing his own hat for the emperor's crown, the fisherman's boy marched off back to the Spanish camp. The king of Spain had to laugh when he saw him, and laughed even more when he entered the Turkish camp and found the emperor sitting turned to stone and wearing the wrong hat. He asked the boy if he could bring him to life again. Then the boy waved the sword over his head in the opposite direction and the emperor came to life and called on his men. But the king laughed louder than ever because none of the Turkish army could move; they were still all turned to stone. In the end, the emperor agreed to pay an enormous ransom and lead his men out of the country, if only they could be released from the spell. And when they had been brought to life, they marched off and Spain was free again.

The king was so pleased with the fisherman's son that there was nothing he would not do for him, and he even made him an admiral of the Spanish fleet. But after a time the fisherman's son, now a great man in Spain, began to long for home and begged the king to release him. Although sorry to lose him, the king would not stop him and even provided a warship for his journey, complete with many guns.

So, sailing home in his fine ship, the fisherman's son anchored opposite the grocer's house and gave orders for all the guns of his ship to be fired, which of course caused a great commotion in the village, where it was feared that an enemy was about to land.

Going ashore in his admiral's uniform, the fisherman's son met an old woman and, giving her a letter with his half of the gold ring, told her to deliver it only to the grocer's daughter, saying he would wait there for her reply.

The woman delivered the letter and the half of the gold ring to the grocer's daughter, and of course the girl was overjoyed to know that her old sweetheart had come home. The grocer needed little persuasion to entertain the admiral of such a rich ship and, invited to dine at the house, the admiral came glittering with gold from top to toe.

After they had dined, the admiral said he would like to tell his host a story. It was, he said, about a poor man and a rich man. The poor man had had so many children he had barely been able to provide for them, while the rich man had an only daughter. The poor man's son had become the sweetheart of the rich man's daughter, but the rich man had done everything he could to part them so that they would never see each other again.

"What sort of punishment do you think the man deserved?" the admiral asked the grocer.

"Why, he deserved to be hanged," the grocer replied.

"You have passed judgment on yourself," said the

admiral, and he told the grocer of his adventures at sea and how he had come to claim his daughter for his bride. The grocer trembled all over when he saw he had condemned himself; but the admiral graciously forgave him, and there was general rejoicing. The wedding took place without further delay, and the poor fisherman and his wife sat at the top table with all the rest.

"There," said the grocer's wife, "now you see. Never say 'never'!"

And she reminded her husband of what he had written on the beam, and of how he had sworn it would never come to pass, though now it had.

As for the daughter, she lived happily with her admiral, the greatest that Spain had ever known, for many and many a year after.

The white cat

Once upon a time in a far distant land there was a king who had three sons. The two eldest were tall and handsome but the young one, who was called Per, was a very ordinary little fellow whom his brothers were always making fun of. The king, however, was just as fond of him as he was of the others.

The king was now growing old, and soon the time must come when he would have to decide which of his three sons should reign when he died; but he just could not make up his mind.

Now, in those days it was the custom to surround the palace with a long chain, to prevent people from wandering carelessly into the palace courtyard. The chain that now surrounded the palace had grown old and rusty, and would soon have to be replaced; and the king, being a sensible king, thought he would kill two birds with one stone. So he said to the three princes: "We really do need a new chain for the palace. I think you should each go and get one. And the one that brings back the biggest and best shall be king when I die. Be off with you, and don't come back till a year has passed."

So off they went.

The eldest prince thought that his best plan would be to go and work for a locksmith, the best and most famous locksmith he could find; while the second prince apprenticed himself to a coppersmith, thinking to himself that copper would be easier to work with than iron. As for Per, he at first was unwilling to go, feeling sure that he would not have any chance against his two clever brothers. But the king insisted; and so he had to go. Having not the remotest idea where to look for a chain, he just wandered off into the forest, where very soon he got lost. The day drew on and night began to fall, and still he just wandered along. Then, straight in front of him, he saw a light; and following this, he arrived at a cottage, where he knocked at the door.

"Come in!" a voice inside called; and in he went.

Imagine his surprise when he opened the door and found nobody in the cottage but a large white cat sitting on a chair. For want of anyone else to ask, Per inquired of the cat if he could have a night's lodging.

"Why, of course," said the cat. "But it's so late in the evening, I think you must be hungry."

Per agreed heartily and so the cat showed him where to find all he wanted and Per made himself a good meal. Then, when he had finished eating, the cat pointed to a bed that was already made up, and said he could sleep there. To Per, all this seemed too good to be true.

When he got up the next morning, the cat asked him who he was and where he was going; and when Per explained, saying he had no idea where to look for the chain he had been told to find, the cat said: "Why not stay with me? All you will have to do is wash and comb me three times a day, and in return you shall have food and lodging, but no other wages."

Well, this sounded like an easy sort of life, so Per agreed. He washed and combed the cat three times a day, and the rest of the time he just roamed the forest. Then, when a year had gone by, the cat said: "Now it's time for you to go home, Per. Your brothers are there already."

Per, however, was unwilling to give up this pleasant life in the forest, especially since he had not succeeded in finding a chain. But the cat said he must.

"I promise you," it went on, "that you shall have as good a chain as either of your brothers. In the passage out there you'll find a chest. Take it with you; and when they have shown your father their chains, just open the chest and see what you find."

So, taking leave of the cat, Per went off home with the chest.

When the three brothers were all gathered together, their father the king asked to see what they had brought, and the eldest prince showed his chain. It was a big heavy one, made of iron; and when they tried it out it just went nicely round the palace.

The second prince then brought out his chain. It was made of copper, and was even longer than his brother's, because it went round the palace and half-way back again.

The two brothers both smiled when it was Per's turn; but when he opened his chest, there, to everyone's surprise, was a magnificent chain that was of the purest gold. And it was long enough to go twice round the palace. They all had to agree that Per had won.

But the elder brothers were dissatisfied; they had been absolutely sure of winning, and they argued that Per was unfit to be king. So in the end the king had to set them all another task. They were to go away and see how much money they could earn in a year. The one who earned the most should inherit the kingdom. So off they went again.

The elder brothers were certain this time that one of them would win, because Per never knew how to keep even his pocket money; he spent it as soon as he got it. The eldest prince decided to become a merchant, and he made big profits on what he bought and sold. The second prince became a moneylender and made even greater profits. Poor Per had no idea what to become; he just went wandering off into the forest as he had done before.

Soon he arrived at the cat's cottage, and began to serve the cat exactly as he had done before. Time passed quickly and pleasantly, and before he knew, the year had gone by.

"Now go home to your father," the cat said one day; "for your brothers have already arrived." And when Per said he had no money to take home with him, the cat told him to go into the passage, where he would find a chest. This he was to take home with him.

His brothers were already showing the king their money when he got there. The eldest prince had brought a huge pile of coppers, which when he spread them out covered half the palace floor. The second prince had brought home a pile of silver money, and this covered the other half of the palace floor.

"Well, Per, can you do better than that?" the king asked.

Per was not so sure; but when he opened his chest they all stared in amazement, because it was full to the brim with gold coins. And when he spread them out they covered the palace floor and not a single copper or silver coin could be seen; the whole palace glittered with gold.

"Well," said the king, "Per has won again. So he shall have the sceptre and crown and reign after me."

But again the elder brothers argued that he was not fit to reign. And they protested so much that, once again, the king had to agree to set them all another task. This time they were to bring back a wife; and the one who returned at the end of the year with the most beautiful wife should inherit the throne, and there would be no more arguing.

This time, the elder princes thought, Per could not possibly win. For who would have that fellow for a husband?

As always, the two elder brothers set off with a purpose; and, as before, Per just wandered off into the forest, until in time he arrived at the same cottage. "Come in!" cried the cat. "Make yourself at home, and serve me for another year as before."

So for another year Per washed and combed the cat three times a day, and spent the rest of the time enjoying himself in the forest.

Then one day the cat said the year was up and he was to go home to his father; his brothers were already there with their brides. But what was the use, Per said, when he had not found a bride?

"Well," said the cat, "you have now served me faithfully and well for three years, so I'm going to help you once more. But you must do as I say. Take that knife and cut my head off; and when you have done that, skin me."

Per said he could not possibly do anything so cruel to someone who had been so kind to him. But the cat said he must, and in the end he had to agree.

So, taking the kitchen knife, he cut off the cat's

head at a single stroke; and was just starting to skin the cat when, in a twinkling, it was gone, and in front of him stood the most beautiful princess. He knew she must be a princess because she was wearing a gold crown.

The princess now told Per that all these years she had been under a spell, which could only be broken when a prince consented to serve her for three years without payment.

"That is what you did," she said. "And now I will go home with you. Let us get into the gold coach that is waiting outside, and I will tell you all about it as we go along."

"My father," she said as Per sat beside her, cracking his whip, "my father was once a great king, and he lived happily together with my mother, the queen. But then she fell ill and died, and my father married another queen who was a widow with a daughter of her own. The new queen was afraid that her own daughter would be put aside in favour of me, and it was she who cast the spell on me and turned me into a cat."

Turning to the princess as she finished her tale, Per was overwhelmed by her beauty and just had to stop the coach, right there in the middle of the forest, to give her a kiss.

The two brothers were already showing off their brides when Per and his princess arrived at the palace. But the moment she stepped from the coach everyone could see that she was easily the most beautiful of them all. So Per inherited the kingdom after all; and with the help and affection of his beautiful wife grew into a very wise king who was much loved by his people. As for the brothers, they went abroad and were never seen again.

Good times and bad

A long, long time ago, St Peter, who keeps the gates of heaven, and who felt that he needed a rest, asked the good Lord if he might have a holiday. He would like, he said, to visit the earth.

The Lord gave his permission, but told him not to stay away too long, for during his absence the gates would have to be kept locked and in that time no-one would be able to gain admittance.

St Peter thanked the Lord and, after handing over his keys and promising to be back soon, descended to earth.

A week went by, and then a fortnight and then a month, and still St Peter had not returned. At last he arrived, and the Lord asked him why he had been so long.

"Well, Lord," said St Peter. "The times on earth were good. There was a plentiful harvest, there was peace among nations and everyone was prosperous."

"Did they remember me?" asked the Lord.

"No," said St Peter. "At least, nobody but an old woman whose cottage had burnt down. But everyone else just laughed at her."

Time passed, and St Peter asked the Lord if he might go down to earth again; the Lord gave his permission, and St Peter descended as before.

This time he was back within a week. And when the Lord asked him why he had returned so soon, St Peter said: "Well, Lord, the times on earth were bad. There were wars and unrest, and many people were starving. Everybody was miserable and unhappy."

"Did nobody remember me?" asked the Lord.

"Oh yes," said St Peter. "Everybody did. They were all on their knees, praying to you for better times."

"There!" said the Lord. "Now you see. Good times must be followed by bad ones, or they will forget me altogether."

The English prince and the Danish princess

A young prince of England chanced to see a picture of the young princess of Denmark and at once he fell deeply in love with her, vowing that he would have none other for his wife. No-one could have been more pleased to hear this than his father, the English king. "With England and Denmark united," he said, "no power on earth can match us."

So the king of England sent a letter to the king of Denmark, requesting his daughter's hand in marriage for his son, who of course would inherit the English throne after his father. But the Danish king answered that his daughter was not grown up yet, nor would she ever become the queen of England.

At this, the English king got very angry, and sent word to say that the Danish princess should be his son's bride cost what it might in blood. For his part, the Danish king declared that no such thing should come about for as long as a single drop of blood flowed in Danish veins.

So now there was war between the two countries and the English prince with a large army invaded

Denmark and besieged the Danish capital. Meanwhile, the Danish king took care to protect his daughter by sending her away to a castle in a distant island; and he walled the castle round so that nobody could reach her, leaving enough food to last her for seven years.

By the end of the seven years the war was over. The English prince had taken the Danish capital and had killed the king. Now he resolved to make the Danish palace his home.

The first thing the English prince did when he occupied the palace was to go through all the rooms in order to find the princess; but of course he did not find her there. What he did find, in her chamber, was an ivory loom, which had spindles of the purest gold; and on the loom was a piece of material that was woven in a beautiful pattern of birds and fishes and all sorts of other creatures. But the weaving had not been finished.

After scouring the country in search of the princess and still not finding her, the English prince sent out messengers, proclaiming that whoever was able to finish the beautiful weaving should be his wife and become queen. Now, surely, the prince thought, the princess would come forward, knowing that she had nothing to fear from him.

It so happened that in Denmark at that time there was a duke whose daughter resembled the vanished princess; and as she was also a skilful weaver, the duke sent her to the palace in order to try her luck. But the pattern proved to be too difficult for her, and no matter how hard she tried, it always came out wrong.

Meanwhile, over in the island castle the princess had consumed all her food. She had succeeded in breaking her way through a part of the castle wall; but it was very hard work, and unless she could soon escape she would be starving. But she kept on, and in time managed to slip out. A ship happened to be passing the island as she did so, and so she took a sheet and waved it till the ship turned and rescued her, putting her off near to her father's palace, which now belonged to the English prince.

Not wishing to make herself known straight away, the princess took off her royal robes and put on some old rags. Then she went round to the kitchen to ask if they needed a kitchen-maid. It was the duke's daughter who answered the door, and, as she liked the look of the girl, she engaged her. And so the princess began work as a scullery maid in her own father's palace, doing the washing-up and all the other unpleasant jobs.

One day the scullery maid, that is to say the princess, was sent on an errand to her old chamber, where the loom stood. There she found the duke's daughter working at the loom, and complaining all the time that the pattern was too complicated. The scullery maid, however, said she thought she could finish the weaving.

"If you can," said the duke's daughter, "I'll give you a hundred florins."

The princess then unwove what the duke's daughter had done wrong, and soon was working away so fast at the loom that the rattling of the shuttle could be heard all over the palace. The prince heard it like everyone else, and thought he would go and see what was going on. And to his great delight, he found that the work was finished and the pattern was perfect. The duke's daughter should now become his wife, he said; for he could hardly imagine that the

ragged scullery maid could have completed the
weaving.

When the wedding day came round, the prince
decided that his bride-to-be should ride beside him
to the church on horseback, but this the duke's
daughter was afraid to do. She ordered the princess,
who by now had advanced to be parlourmaid, to take
off her old clothes and put on the wedding dress
instead. They would then change places at the
church. And for this the parlourmaid would receive
another hundred florins.

So, dressed as the bride, the princess rode off to
the church, with the prince riding beside her.

Soon they came to a bridge; and it was so old that
it creaked and groaned at the slightest breeze.

> Bridge, bridge, break not for me!
> My father it was who erected thee,

said the princess; and the bridge held up till they had
crossed over.

"What did you say, my dear?" the prince asked.

"Nothing, my lord," replied the princess.

Next they came to a castle, where a watchdog at the gate barked furiously at them.

> Dog, dog, bark not at me!
> My father it was who fed thee,

said the princess; and the dog stopped barking.

"What did you say, my dear?" the prince asked.

"Nothing, my lord," replied the princess.

Riding on, they came to the castle moat; and there the princess said:

> Here in the water so clean
> Swim fishes so lovely and green.

"What did you say, my dear?" the prince asked.

"Nothing, my lord," replied the princess.

Still they rode on, and now, far away in the distance, the princess could just make out the island where she had lived for seven long years. Now, the princess had once possessed a horse, whose name was Blankie; and during the seven long years she had lived in the castle, this horse had been left to look after itself, and had grown so wild that it took two grooms, exerting all their strength, to drag it down to be watered.

Now, as the prince and the princess came riding along, they saw Blankie; and it was rearing and kicking and behaving very badly indeed.

> Blankie, dear, kneel down for me;
> It was I that used to ride thee,

said the princess. And the moment the horse heard the princess's voice, it knelt down and she got on its back.

"What did you say, my dear?" asked the prince.

"Nothing, my lord," replied the princess.

Now, however, the prince was very happy, because by this time he felt sure that the person who rode beside him could be none other than the princess of Denmark.

The prince had been wearing gloves that were made of gold, and when they arrived at the church he took them off and gave them to the princess, making her swear that she, and she alone, would return the gloves to him when he asked for them.

After the wedding there was to have been a grand feast, but the prince said he was not in the mood for merrymaking and asked all the wedding guests to return the next day, when they would celebrate the happy event in the proper fashion. Meanwhile the duke's daughter took the princess's place, sending her back to the kitchen.

When the prince retired with the duke's daughter to the bridal chamber that evening, he asked her to repeat the words she had spoken at the bridge, but the duke's daughter pleaded that she was so excited by all the day's events that her memory had gone. However, her parlourmaid would know. So she went to the princess, and said: "Tell me, girl, what was it you said at the bridge?" And the princess told her. Whereupon she told it to the prince.

The prince then asked what she had said to the dog; and again the duke's daughter had to go and get the answer from the princess.

"You have a wonderful maid who can remember everything so well," said the prince; "but I would also like to know what you said at the moat." And of course the duke's daughter had to go and ask the princess again.

The prince then asked the duke's daughter what

she had said to the horse; and after asking her maid, the princess, she said:

> Blankie, dear, kneel down for me;
> It was I that used to ride thee.

The duke's daughter now thought that as she had answered all the questions correctly the prince would be satisfied. But then he asked for the golden gloves he had given her. She would go and get them, she said. The princess, however, said she could not give them to her, because she had sworn only to return them to the prince himself. But she agreed to go with the duke's daughter to the bridal chamber and hand them to the prince after first putting out the lights. Then she would leave the room, and of course the prince would think that he had got the gloves from the duke's daughter.

So when all the lights had been put out, the princess handed the gloves to the prince as they had arranged. But before the room could be lit up again, the prince caught the princess by the hand and commanded the other person in the room to leave it. He had understood everything.

Next morning, the deceitful daughter of the duke was sent packing to her father; and at the palace a magnificent banquet was held to celebrate the marriage of the English prince to the Danish princess, and with it the union of great England and Denmark.

The girl and the snake

Once upon a time a young girl was sent with some food for her father, who was ploughing in the field. When she got there, he asked her to fetch him his coat, which lay under a tree. So she went to get it.

When she got to the tree, however, she found a huge snake lying on the coat. Picking up a stick, she tried to drive it off, but it refused to budge. She then pleaded with it to go away, so she could take the coat to her father.

"All right, then," said the snake; "if you will promise to return and sit on my back, you shall have it." So the girl promised; and after taking the coat to her father, returned to the snake, which told her to sit on its back, as she had promised. So she did so; and the snake went hurrying off with her into the forest and along paths the girl had never seen before. After it had hurried along like this for some time, the snake said: "Little girl, stand up on my back and tell me if you can see anything."

The girl did as she was told, and said she could see something that shone like silver.

"That's my mother's palace," said the snake. "We've a long way to go yet." And off it hurried.

After a while it stopped and said: "Stand up on my back and tell me if you see anything."

The girl said she could see something that shone like gold.

"That's my father's palace," said the snake. "We've a long way to go yet." And off it hurried.

Soon it stopped for a third time, saying: "Stand up on my back and tell me if you see anything."

The girl said she could see something that sparkled like diamonds.

"Ah, now we'll soon be there," said the snake. And off it hurried.

Soon they came to a splendid palace.

"Now," said the snake, "stand up on my back and ring the bell. And when the gatekeeper comes and asks what you want, tell him you would like to serve at the palace."

So the girl rang the bell; and when the gatekeeper asked her what she could do, she said she could sweep the floors and carry water and give a hand in the kitchen, and the gatekeeper said that she would do.

When she had gone to bed that evening, she heard something rustle at the door, and she got up to see what it was.

"It's me," said the snake. "It's so cold out here, and I'm freezing. Won't you let me in?"

So the girl let it in and slipped back into bed. No sooner had she done so than it crawled to her bedside and, raising its head, seemed as if it wanted to kiss her. And it looked at her so pleadingly that she felt that she had to. So, holding a corner of the sheet to her lips, she kissed the snake on its horrid slimy mouth. And, in a twinkling, the snake was transformed into a handsome young prince. He was so grateful to the girl; and saying that this was his palace, he told her how he had been bewitched.

In time, the prince and the girl who had broken the witch's spell by her kiss were married, and there was great rejoicing. After the wedding, they travelled first to his father's palace and then to his mother's, and from there to the girl's parents, whom they invited to join them at their very own palace, where they all lived happily ever after.

A trusty sword

A poor man lay dying; and calling his only son to his bedside, he said: "My son, I have very little to leave you. This cottage, when you sell it, will pay for my burial, and the only other thing I possess is that sword which you see hanging over there. But it is a rather special sword. With it, you will defeat all your enemies. Take care of it."

And with those words he died.

The sword was an old and rusty one, but the man's son treasured it and took it with him when he set out in search of work. In time, he got work as a shepherd boy.

Now, when he went out on the first day with his flock, his master gave him this warning: "Beware of the three furthest pastures. They belong to the mountain giants who live in the hill; and if only one of your sheep strays into their pastures, one of the giants will come out and carry off both the sheep and you."

The last was said in order to frighten the boy, because in fact it was only the sheep that would be lost. But the boy took heed and not a single sheep was lost.

One day, the boy had the idea that he would try out his sword if the giant appeared; so he deliberately allowed one of the sheep to stray into the furthest pastures.

Immediately a horrible giant came rushing out, as he roared: "Who gave you permission to drive your sheep into my pasture?"

"Nobody," said the boy. "I took permission myself."

"Then you are not going to get out alive," the giant shouted.

But the shepherd boy just took his sword and cut the giant in two. Now his sheep had the whole pasture to themselves.

Soon after this, the boy's sheep strayed into the

101

next pasture, and he followed them. At once the second giant came rushing out.

"Who gave you permission to drive your sheep into my pasture?" he roared.

"Nobody," said the boy. "I took permission myself."

"Was it you who killed my brother?" shouted the giant.

"Yes," said the boy "with this sword."

"Then I shall kill you," roared the giant. But before he could do anything, the shepherd boy had cut him in two.

Exactly the same thing happened when the sheep strayed into the third pasture. The giant rushed out and threatened, but got cut in two.

Now, the next day the shepherd boy thought he would like to have a look at the giants' hill, and so he crept in through a hole in the hillside and found himself in a giant cave. In it there were three horses – one red, one yellow and one white – as well as three dogs, also one red, one yellow and one white. There were saddles and coats of mail for the horses, each in the same colours. In addition there was a plentiful supply of food for both the horses and the dogs, together with large quantities of gold and silver. The boy was delighted to see all this splendour, and that evening sang merrily as he drove his flock home.

Coming out to meet him, his master told him how pleased he was with his work, though he warned him not to sing. He then told the boy about a promise the king had been forced into making. This was that his three daughters were to be given up to three sea-trolls who would soon be coming to fetch them. The king had proclaimed that whoever succeeded in saving one of his daughters should have a third of his

102

kingdom and the daughter's hand in marriage. But he had little hope that anyone would succeed and in his grief he had commanded that there should be no more singing or public rejoicing.

The next day the shepherd boy went into town to see how matters lay, and there he learnt that the eldest daughter was to be taken and handed over to the first of the sea-trolls the very next day. The following morning, therefore, the boy went to the giants' hill where he put on the red coat of mail, mounted the red horse and, taking the red dog with him, rode off to the place where the troll would appear from the sea.

Presently, the princess came riding in a gold coach down to the shore. There the coach stopped and the coachman on hearing the approaching sea-troll hid in a tree. At that moment up rode the shepherd boy on his red horse and with his trusty sword cut off all three of the sea-troll's heads. Then after cutting out their tongues, he rode off with them. Meanwhile, the coachman had recovered from his fright; and climbing down the tree, made the princess promise to say that it was he who killed the sea-troll. Then they drove back to the palace. There there was great rejoicing and the coachman got much praise for his bravery and was promised the princess's hand in marriage.

A week later, the second princess was taken down to the shore and, when the second sea-troll came to claim her, this coachman, too, hid in a tree. But then a yellow horseman, who was none other than the same shepherd boy, came riding up on a yellow horse, cut off the sea-troll's heads, all six of them, and rode off with their tongues. This coachman, also, made the princess promise to say that he had killed the sea-troll.

Exactly the same things took place when, a week later, the third princess was driven down to the shore. The coachman hid in a tree, and a white horseman rode up on a white horse, and cut off the sea-troll's nine heads. But just as he was riding off with the tongues, the princess threw him her gold chain, and it was caught up in his hair. The third coachman, too, made the princess say he had saved her.

There was now great rejoicing at the palace; and hearing of the festivities that were to take place when the three princesses were married, all three on the same day, the shepherd boy decided he would go and find out all about them. He put up at an inn near the palace.

"I wouldn't mind having a taste of the wheaten bread they'll be having up at the palace," the inn-keeper said.

"I'll send my dog for some," the boy said. So away went the red dog; and after running all through the palace till it found the room where the bread was kept, it snatched a loaf and ran back to the inn with it.

"I wouldn't mind having a taste of the roast beef they'll be having up at the palace," the innkeeper said the next day. So the shepherd boy sent off his yellow dog; and after running all through the palace till it found where they kept the meat, it snatched up a leg of beef from under the cook's nose and ran back to the inn with it.

On the third day, which was the actual day of the wedding, the innkeeper said he wouldn't mind a bottle of wine from the palace. So the shepherd boy sent off his white dog to get one; and after running all through the palace till it found the banqueting hall, where the wedding guests were already seated, it snatched a bottle from the table and ran back with it to the inn.

Now, when the youngest princess saw the white dog she clapped her hands and cried that it was the dog's master who had saved her from the sea-troll.

"Ridiculous!" said the bridegroom. "You know I saved you."

"Oh no," she said, "it wasn't you. You made me say it was, but it was the dog's master."

"Follow the dog and see where it goes," commanded the king.

So off the king's footmen ran, puffing and blowing, after the dog, and of course it led them to the inn and its master, the shepherd boy. They then took the boy straight back to the palace, but he at first refused to enter, saying he was too rough for such fine company. The king, however, ordered him to come in.

"Yes, you were my saviour," the princess said. "Where is the gold chain you got from me?"

After holding out the gold chain for everybody to see, the shepherd boy also produced the nine tongues he had cut from the trolls' heads; and then nobody doubted that he was the brave rider who had killed the sea-trolls and rescued the princesses.

So the three cheating coachmen were taken out and hanged; while the shepherd boy married the youngest of the three princesses and was granted the third of the kingdom that had been promised.

A man in the kitchen

In a small village many years ago, there lived a man and his wife who were never content. He thought that she had too easy a time, and she thought that he did. So one day they agreed to take one another's place, just for one day, and see. She would work in the fields, and he would do the housekeeping, churn the butter, look after the cow and cook the meal.

Now, after churning the butter for a time the man began to feel thirsty, and he went down into the cellar for a drink. But he had just turned the beer tap on when he heard a frightful commotion in the kitchen upstairs, and he went up to see what was going on, forgetting, however, to turn off the tap. Of course the beer flowed all over the cellar floor.

In the kitchen, he found that the pig had got in and had knocked over the churn, so the cream was running all over the floor. So he had to skim off some more cream from the milk and start all over again.

He had just nicely begun when he remembered it was time to put the porridge on for dinner; but afraid to leave the churn unattended this time while he fetched water from the well, he took it with him, carrying it on his back. But as he stooped down to draw water from the well, all the cream ran out of the churn and down the well. That was the last of the cream.

When he got back to the kitchen and had put the porridge on to cook, he remembered that he should have taken the cow out to graze, and he ran to get it. But he couldn't think where to take it. However, he knew there was some grass growing on the thatch of their cottage, and so he took the cow up there. It then occurred to him that the cow might fall off the roof; so lowering the rope down the chimney, he tied the other end of it round his leg, thinking that if the cow should happen to fall he would know. He then turned to stirring the porridge.

But no sooner had he done so than the cow did fall, and as it fell it pulled the man up the chimney. There he hung, half-way up, while the cow at the other end hung just above the ground.

Soon, the woman came walking home from the field, eagerly looking forward to her dinner; and seeing the cow hanging there in the air, she ran and cut the rope that held it. For how could she know that the other end was holding her husband in the chimney? He fell head first into the porridge. And from that day they never again changed jobs.

A strange fish

A man went fishing and caught a huge pike. He was so delighted with his catch that he hardly knew what to do with it. It seemed a pity to eat it, and anyway it was far too big for that.

At last he had an idea. He would make a pet of the fish. So he put it in a pool of water. He then had another idea. He thought that if, day by day, he gradually reduced the amount of water in the pool, it might be possible to teach the pike to do without any water at all.

That is exactly what happened. It took a long time, but in the end the pike had learnt to live without water and had become a land animal.

Now, having taught the fish to live on land, the man next thought it should be possible to teach it to walk. And so he did. After a while, the pike could be seen at the man's heels, following him around just like a pet dog. The man was very proud of his pet.

But pride and joy do not last for ever. One day, when the man was out walking, and the pike was trotting along behind him on its lead, they came to a deep ditch. The man was able to stride over it, but the pike tumbled in; and as it had forgotten how to swim, the poor creature was drowned.

Afterword

My tales were told for children, but there
had to be something for the grown-up as well.
Hans Christian Andersen

When the Grimm brothers, Jakob and Wilhelm, published
the first volumes of their *Kinder- und Hausmärchen* in
1812–14, the fruit of thirteen years of patient collecting
and transcribing of folk tales in the regions of Hesse and
Hanover, it will hardly have occurred to them that they
were starting a movement which would spread to virtually
every country in Europe. Here was material, hitherto
despised by the educated classes but cherished in the folk
memory of the illiterate, which in the dawning age of
Romanticism would nourish and inspire a whole line of
novelists and story-tellers, from E. T. A. Hoffmann and
Adalbert von Chamisso in Germany to Hans Christian
Andersen in Denmark not to mention their many imitators.
Collections of folk tales would henceforth provide enter-
taining reading for both young and old.

Following the example of the Grimms, successive collectors were active in Denmark in the latter half of the nine-
teenth century and the beginning of the twentieth. The
outstanding names here are Svend Grundtvig (1824–83),
Evald Tang Kristensen (1843–1929) and Axel Olrik
(1864–1917). Tang Kristensen alone published a pro-
digious collection in over a hundred volumes, mostly at
his own expense. Some of the more popular of these
collectors' tales have been told and retold by later Danish
writers.

In compiling the present collection, I have for the most

part gone back to the yellowed pages and the gothic script of Grundtvig's three pioneering volumes that were published between 1876 and 1884, and I have also included stories from various other original sources. Some basic tales will be immediately recognizable. Like folk tales everywhere, many of the ones in this book embody conventional elements of the miraculous, and many of them are peopled by giants, fairies, "little folk" and such-like supernatural creatures. The magic figure three, of deep significance to the mind of primitive man, recurs predictably, at times perhaps wearisomely, in tale after tale, varied occasionally with the only slightly less magical seven or nine. Nearly always there are three sons or daughters, who have three wishes, or are allowed three attempts. Third time lucky! Other basic features are talking animals, spells cast by witches or wizards, the metamorphosis of errant humans and their re-transformation after penance or repentance, the ill-treated stepchild, the arduous journey in quest of some magic object.

How many of the tales were local in origin no-one can say. Certainly not all of them. Some, indeed, are clearly international in character and form, having been given a local habitation and a degree of local colour. This is not surprising when one bears in mind that there have always been cross-border travellers, and that it is only mass travel that is new. All through the Middle Ages, for instance, Danes drove their bullocks to market in Germany along the central Jutland road that is still known as the Army Road, because it was also the route taken by armies moving south or north. Further back still, as far back as Roman and prehistoric times, merchants journeyed from Denmark as far as the Mediterranean, trading the prized amber, the fossilized resin of Baltic pine-trees, for bronze and even gold. Thus, in book-less days, tales would cross and re-cross frontiers orally, untaxed and uncensored, but subject to constant change and the individual shaping of every new reteller.

The two little pieces about the men of Mols, for example,

belong to an international genre with a venerable pedigree. They parallel our own English tales of the "wise" men of Gotham and German counterparts in the *Schildbürger*. The type is at least as old as classical Greece, where the Abderites were proverbial for their lack of wit.

The name of Hans Christian Andersen has already been cited, and it springs naturally to mind whenever folk tales are mentioned. Unlike the Grimms, Grundtvig and the rest, he was neither a collector nor simply a reteller, but a creative writer of genius. His first little volume of tales was published in 1835, thus anticipating Grundtvig by some forty years. Some of the early ones adhere closely to the basic fairy tale, and some are deliberately based on individual folk tales Andersen had heard in childhood, though even in these this own voice and accents can be heard right from the start.

This book could have been titled "Folk and Fairy Tales" and I am aware that there are scholars who would distinguish between "folk" and "fairy" on the ground that stories about kings and queens, princes and princesses, were not originally *folk* tales, but that they filtered down to the "folk" from the courtly upper classes. We are here on speculative and highly debatable ground, however, and I take the view that it is not really possible to draw any sharp dividing line.

In retelling these tales, I have added nothing to the plot or story line itself, nor in any way altered the general sequence of events, nor introduced any embellishments of my own. But, it has to be remembered that these stories have passed through many hands – or lips – before they were collected, and that they were mostly taken down from old country people who were apt to be prolix and repetitious. While careful to preserve the intrinsic character of the folk tale, I have tried generally to condense and tighten up the narrative, so as to achieve a style more acceptable to a modern audience.

Reginald Spink